The

DAVID WINTER COTTAGES

HANDBOOK
1992-93

JOHN HUGHES

Kevin Francis
Printed in the U K

ACKNOWLEDGMENTS

In compiling this book I have received help from many people, and I would like to thank them all. Not surprisingly the largest thanks by far go to the two main protagonists – David Winter and John Hine. David allowed me periodically to fire barrages of questions at him over several months, clarifying many details about his work and reading the first draft copy. John Hine sanctioned the project in the first place, provided me with information about 'David Winters' that I didn't even know existed, racked his brains to recall details of the past thirteen years and allowed me to reproduce photographs from the John Hine Studios library.

Ian Wetherby-Blythe, of Castle China Shop in Warwick, provided me with a large amount of information from his encyclo-paedic knowledge of both David Winter Cottages and John Hine Studios. Without his input this book would be several pages thinner.

Audrey White kindly answered many questions for me, and so too did Jonno Suart, Tim Moore and Brenda Denton. David Gravelle not only answered questions but rooted in dark cupboards for old files, invoices and price lists, and Shirley Purnell also tracked down numerous documents for me.

Others have made a range of contributions, from supplying secondary market prices to trusting me with their rare and valuable pieces: Chris Billins, Pat Cantrell, Sherrie Carr, David Cohen, John Coles, Pia Colon, Lynne D'Orange, Milton Gold, Ann Hamlet, Denise Hutchings, Sue Jelfs, Nicholas Rink, Patty & Bill Sauers, James G Summers... If I have missed anyone, please forgive me.

I must also acknowledge Messrs. Kevin Pearson and Francis Salmon for agreeing to publish the fruits of my labour.

Finally thanks to my wife Chris, for being so tolerant as I shut myself away during evenings and weekends, trying to put this all down in some order! Now, hopefully, she can see that it's all been worthwhile.

Unless otherwise stated, all photography is by Glenn Blackman.

Illustrations are by Hilary McDonald.

Kevin Francis Publishing
© John Hughes 1992
Production and design Francis Salmon
Compilation James Scannell

Printed in England by
Greenwich Press, London

This book is dedicated to my mother, with love.

About the Author

John Hughes was born in the Midlands town of Sutton Coldfield in 1956. He studied music at Royal Holloway College in Surrey and gained an Honours Degree there. After a short spell working in a bank, he joined Harrods department store selling pianos and electronic keyboards. For three years he was Departmental Manager.

In 1984 he met John Hine and worked with him on a variety of musical projects, including the album *Silver and White*. The following year he joined John Hine Limited, originally to develop the music recording side of the business, but soon found himself side-stepping into the fascinating world of David Winter Cottages. He has been involved with the Collectors Guild since its inception in 1987, primarily as Assistant Editor of the Guild magazine, *Cottage Country*, and has worked on every issue. As well as collaborating editorially with John Hine, he has also spoken many times with David Winter about the inspiration and ideas behind his work, whilst preparing articles for *Cottage Country*. In 1992 he took on the additional responsibilities of U.K. Guild Manager.

John and his wife, Chris, live in Surrey. They have two daughters, Helen and Alice.

CONTENTS

INTRODUCTION

The rise of David Winter Cottages from parochial craft to household name is a delightful success story, and one of many that were the product of 1980s resourcefulness – but the speed at which they have become valuable collectables is unique. There is surely no precedent to the pace at which 'retired' Cottages have mushroomed in value. Some pieces that sold originally in the shop for under £10.00 have now increased in value two hundred times or more. Such is the phenomenon of David Winter Cottages as they enter only their thirteenth year in existence!

Six or seven years ago, 'David Winter' collectors were a relatively small group of people, mainly in Great Britain, who delighted in having these inexpensive, handmade models of traditional English cottages on shelves or cabinets in their homes. The fundamental appeal was, and still is, the mass of fine detail and sheer character that David Winter imparts to his sculptures.

Then something happened. The number of collectors, mainly in North America, mushroomed and generated an enthusiasm for David Winter Cottages as collectables on a scale which we British find difficult to imagine. At about the same time, the discontinuation of Tythe Barn seemed to spark an urgency in collectors' desire for early cottages, especially the ones which were no longer available and made in small production runs. Since then, in the space of a few short years, a thriving secondary market has developed and collecting David Winter Cottages has become a financial investment as well as a matter of artistic appreciation.

This enormous demand for David Winter Cottages has surprised nobody more than the sculptor himself, David Winter, and the man whose company produces the handmade copies of his originals, John Hine. They had no idea what they were unleashing when they made **Mill House** in 1980. Their intention was to make a living out of there new venture; but they did much, much more – they opened an entirely new field in the world of giftware and affordable collectables.

Of course it took a while to get it right; the very first Cottages were not the finely detailed pieces of recent years. Some, frankly, just did not sell and were quickly withdrawn. Ironically these are the pieces that today are the most valuable of all.

Miniature cottages were on the market before David Winter Cottages, but they were mainly earthenware, which is incapable of retaining fine detail. The use of gypsum cast in flexible silicon moulds overcame that problem and made David Winter Cottages possible. The technique itself wasn't new, but its application in the market place was. Furthermore, cheap products of yesteryear had given the medium a bad name, but using the gypsum derivative to create a finely detailed end product broke this stigma. More importantly, here was something affordable with mass appeal which opened the eyes of many to the notion of collecting for the first time.

Just as David Winter Cottages filled a gap in the market (or rather created its own gap), I hope in this book to help fill collectors' insatiable desire for more knowledge about the sculptures they own or aspire to own.

Prices and valuations are only a part of it, and for those collectors who may feel that pieces are being ignored at the expense of monetary concerns, I have included as much information about the Cottages themselves as possible – some of it has never before been published.

This is not a definitive catalogue of everything David Winter has ever sculpted, but it is fairly close. So whether you enjoy David Winter Cottages for their aesthetic value or as a worthwhile investment, there should be something of interest here for you.

John Hine

David Winter

Audrey's Tea Room, only available for a few weeks before the master moulds were tragically destroyed by fire. Consequently it was withdrawn on March 26 1992

1 - THE HISTORY OF DAVID WINTER COTTAGES

There is a tide in the affairs of men,
Which, taken at the flood, leads on to fortune
William Shakespeare

David Winter was born on 18th December 1958 at Catterick in Yorkshire. His father was in the army, and regular postings meant that his childhood was spent in some of the most beautiful English counties; Yorkshire, Kent, Hampshire and Surrey. He developed an early love for the countryside and an awareness of the richness of rural life, and with extended periods spent in Singapore and Malaysia there also came the opportunity to recognise from personal experience the distinctive nature of traditional British architecture.

Both David and his sister Alice inherited artistic talent from their mother, Faith Winter, a sculptor of international reputation, and David has been "making things" for as long as he can remember. On leaving school, it was a natural progression for him to assist in his mother's studio, and it was here that he learned the techniques and skills of his craft.

In the summer of 1979, aged twenty, he was making pottery and 'spun' ceramic tiles (spinning them on a potter's wheel and dripping paint onto them to create spiral patterns) which he then sold from a stall in Guildford market. They were popular but not very profitable. It was then that he met John Hine.

John had recently sold his interest in a garden centre and had time on his hands to develop an idea he had that three-dimensional heraldic plaques might be a saleable commodity. In the garden centre John had displayed several of Faith's beautiful garden sculptures, including a sculpture of Pan which had not sold; and on returning it to her John put forward his proposal for making heraldic plaques.

At the time Faith was rather busy, so she passed the suggestion on to David. He made a plaque as a test using a silicon rubber mould (which he already knew how to make) and cast it in a material often used by Faith in her studio – a hard and durable gypsum plaster given the trade name *Crystacal* by the manufacturer, British Gypsum. David remembers being very nervous when he showed the plaque to John Hine, but John was delighted with what he saw. Their working partnership had begun.

Meanwhile John Hine made a lucky find. He needed a painter for the project and so advertised in his local paper, the *Surrey Advertiser*. It was answered by Audrey White, a professional painter who was looking for work again having raised a family. John left a sample plaque with her and returned a week later to see the results. He knew when he saw her work that he had his painter – and the most fortunate omen for the future was that in her previous career Audrey had specialised in miniatures.

Through the late summer and autumn of 1979 the heraldry project progressed, with John Hine organising the sculpting and casting at the Winters' home and the painting at Audrey White's. Their work culminated in an exhibition in Guildford three days before Christmas. It was a total disaster, with not a single piece sold.

They were undeterred. Early in the New Year came a bust of Prince Charles, sculpted by Faith, cast by David Winter and available in three different finishes. John trudged around gift shops trying to generate interest, but again, reaction was unfavourable. (This was not helped by an error in calculating the centre of gravity of the bust which gave it a natural tendency to fall over!) So one day, in a shop in St Catherine's Dock, London, John asked the disinterested owner: "All right, if this won't sell, tell me what *will* sell!" The man showed him a ceramic butter dish made in the shape of a traditional thatched cottage, and replied: "Here. Cottage shapes sell."

That evening the butter dish was with David Winter, who found the whole idea of sculpting miniature cottages very exciting indeed. A mill was decided upon as a test piece – it was old-fashioned, slightly romantic, and reflected a way of life that no longer existed – all themes that appealed to both John and David. David spent a long time working on the sculpture, using bits and pieces to create the effects he needed as he went along; lace for the crown of the thatch, matchsticks for beams, and even shoring up the model with matchboxes because he didn't have enough wax. Eventually the piece was finished, and a square sign at the front declared it to be:

THE
MILL HOUSE
ENGLAND
© DAVID WINTER

Mill House was taken by John Hine to a gift shop called *David Windsor* at 201 High Street, Guildford, Surrey, on 10th March 1980. The owner was pessimistic about selling it but agreed to display it in his window on a sale-or-return basis, with a price tag of £7.50. To his surprise, however, it sold the same afternoon. He phoned John Hine and asked for two more. John and David were equally surprised – and delighted – and promptly spent twice their earnings from the sale in celebrating their success.

In the sober light of morning, David Windsor's were supplied with two more Mill Houses. In a matter of days David and John had a second stockist, *Spectrum Gallery* in Dorking, Surrey, and within a week Mill House was in at least half-a-dozen shops. David sculpted some more pieces (**Dove Cottage** came second, then **Three Ducks Inn** and **The Forge**), and gradually a chain of stockists developed. It is by now a well-worn cliché to say that this was a "cottage industry", but the description is very apt. The Cottages were sculpted and cast in a converted coalshed next to David's parents' house, where he then lived, Audrey painted them in her living room and John Hine made deliveries and drove around selling them to the shops. There was no initial capital; only when they had cash from selling Cottages could they purchase Crystacal, silicon rubber for moulds and paint to make more.

Apart from the very first Mill House, which David Winter painted himself, Audrey White painted every other Cottage in the first six months. She remembers starting off with batches of three or four, but as 1980 progressed orders gradually increased, and to keep up with the demand, production had to continue round the clock. A regular routine was established whereby last thing at night Audrey would leave painted Cottages in the cat box outside her back door and John would collect them at 5am the next morning, replacing them with more unpainted models. Overnight, the cottages had been drying on the storage heater in John's house.

For the heraldic plaques acrylic paints had been used. However, they were not suitable for the Cottages and another style had to be developed. Powder paints mixed with water were tried, but the effect was too dull. Then David suggested mixing the powder paints with white polish and methylated spirits. This gave a slight sheen to the Cottages and had the additional benefit of 'floating' the paint into all the tiny crevices. It worked beautifully, and this basic formula is the one still used today.

By the summer of 1980 it became apparent that more hands were needed, and additional people were drafted in to help. Two new painters were hired and trained by Audrey, and Anthony Wyatt and David Gravelle joined to help John Hine spread the net of stockists wider. By the end of the year, David had also sculpted (in this order) **Little Mill**, **Little Forge**, **The Tiny Series**, **Market Street**, **Little Market**, **The Winemerchant**, **Quayside**, **The Coaching Inn** and **Rose Cottage**. David Winter Cottages had ceased to be an untried experiment and were developing into a valid product in the giftware market.

The coalshed had by now outgrown its requirements and early in 1981 a converted shop was taken on at 19 Ash Street, Ash, a village just outside Aldershot. David had a studio there and all mouldmaking, casting and painting was done on the premises. **Single**, **Double** and **Triple Oast** were amongst the first pieces sculpted at Ash Street. David was adding more and more detail and experimenting all the time (**Chichester Cross** was quite a challenge!), and during 1981 he crystallised the true style of David Winter Cottages. The piece in which he felt he achieved this was **Stratford House**. Confirmation (if any were needed) came with the first substantial order from the *Chinacraft* chain of stores. At about this time John Hine became a limited company, with *David Winter Cottages* as a trade name. This was later extended into *The Studios and Workshops of John Hine Limited*. Yet another milestone was reached towards the end of the year when David sculpted **The Village**, which is still regarded by many as his masterpiece.

1982 saw a further move into larger premises, at Hendon Road, Bordon. This is a town about twelve miles from Aldershot, and David worked there in a new studio. (Ash Street was retained for various activities under the separate heading of *John Hine Creative Limited.*) By this time the network of 'homepainters' had been developed, whereby trays of white stock (unpainted cottages) were delivered to trained painters in their homes, where they could work at their own pace and in familiar surroundings. It also allowed housewives and part-time workers to practice talents they might otherwise not have known they possessed. A mixture of 'in-house' painters and homepainters is still used by John Hine Studios.

For the next three years David continued to sculpt a flow of pieces mainly inspired by regions or crafts and trades – **Sussex Cottage** (1982), **The Bakehouse** (1983), **Tollkeeper's Cottage** (1984), **Kent Cottage** (1985) and **The Apothecary Shop** (1985). Interspersed amongst them were prestige pieces that continued to develop David Winter's technique as a sculptor and the ability of the mouldmaking team to reproduce them in Crystacal – **The Old Distillery** (1982), **Fairytale Castle** (1982), **The Parsonage** (1984).

In the autumn of 1982 an American store owner, Christine Kuyper, saw David Winter Cottages in Harrods, London, and was so impressed that she asked to be put in touch with the makers. As a result, she placed an order with John Hine and in December her store, *The English Center*, in Bellvue, Washington, became the first stockist of David Winter's work in North America.

The following year an office was established in Vancouver, Canada, and during the mid-80s exports to North America began to flourish. The increase in demand that this infinitely greater market created led to the largest move yet – to a series of premises in Woolmer Way, Bordon, less than a mile from Hendon Road. The first building was acquired in early 1985.

In the same year David sculpted the eleven pieces known as 'The Heart of England Series'. By now he too had moved out of Hendon Road and established a studio at his home, which was next door to his parents' home and a matter of yards away from the coalshed where David Winter Cottages began. He has worked in his 'home studio' ever since, and only a couple of pieces in recent years have been sculpted elsewhere (**Orchard Cottage** was sculpted at Eggars Hill and several pieces have been worked upon at David's holiday cottage in Ireland).

Work began in 1986 on the 'West Country Collection', the first five of which were released the following year. An additional two were added in 1988, the same year that a second 'regional' set appeared – 'The Midlands Collection' (six pieces). Then came 'The Scottish Collection' (five pieces) in 1989 and the largest Collection to date, 'British Traditions', which consists of twelve pieces inspired by British customs, released throughout 1990. David's long awaited 'Irish Collection' finally appeared in 1992.

David continued to challenge the skills of the mouldmakers. One piece from the 'West Country Collection', **Smugglers Creek**, was a particularly difficult piece to make. Its technical achievement was recognised and admired by collectors, and at *The California Plate and Collectible Show* held in Pasadena in 1987, Smugglers Creek won the 'Best Collectible of the Show' award. John Hine remarked at the time: "What's a Collectible, and what's a Pasadena?" He soon learned, and it was the beginning of an association with North American Collectors' shows that has continued to strengthen ever since. It was also the first of many awards.

Towards the end of the 1980s David Winter Cottages had established an enormous following. To appease a growing desire for information about David and his work, and to help give collectors an 'identity', the *David Winter Cottages Collectors Guild* was launched in 1987, offering pieces exclusively to Guild Members and supplying information through the quarterly Guild magazine, *Cottage Country*. This coincided with the first of the annual limited edition Christmas pieces, **Ebenezer Scrooge's Counting House**, which has proved to be amongst David's most popular models.

1988 was the year John Hine North America moved its base from Vancouver to Houston, Texas. Four years on it remains the centre of administration and distribution for David Winter Cottages in the USA. Canada is now administered by Royal Selangor Inc. in Rexdale, Ontario and Australia by Selangor Pewter in Bayswater, Victoria.

Whilst Woolmer Way established itself as the mainstay of John Hine's Workshops, the studio side had also been developing. Early in 1986 work began on converting a seventeenth century barn and adjoining derelict buildings into offices and studios for *John Hine Creative Limited*. The house next door was also purchased and became John's home. This is Eggars Hill, the current home of what is now referred to as *John Hine Studios*, a title that is today the most commonly used for the company that makes David Winter Cottages.

Since then the site has been virtually rebuilt, (all but the barn), and has been restored and developed into its current role as a visitors centre for collectors of David Winter Cottages. It also houses the work of numerous other artists that John Hine has discovered over the past ten years. Although David still chooses to work in his home studio, Audrey White worked at Eggars Hill from late 1986 until her retirement in August 1991, and many collectors had the opportunity to meet and talk with her. (The origination of colours for new David Winter Cottages is now undertaken by Kerry Agar.) A further attraction remains the complete display of all David's retired pieces, some of which are very rare indeed. A complete display, that is, apart from Provencal Two!. And the number of visitors has been steadily growing: in 1991 over four thousand visitors came to Eggars Hill.

Whereas Eggars Hill has remained the sole location of the Studios, the Workshops have seen considerable changes. Woolmer Way expanded into several adjoining units and into a small building at Alton, five miles away. Then in 1989, due to spiralling costs and a need to seek out fresh sources of homepainters, small workshops were established at Southampton and Newcastle-upon-Tyne to paint Cottages and a large one for casting and painting at Wrexham in North Wales. Since then there has been what amounts to a relocation of the production side of David Winter Cottages, with a gradual diminishing of Bordon's role and Wrexham becoming the base.

David Winter's resourcefulness in coming up with new and exciting work remains undiminished, and 1991 saw the emergence of a remarkable sculpture – **CASTLE IN THE AIR**. Ten years after **The Village** was hailed as his masterpiece, many collectors feel that **CASTLE IN THE AIR** has taken on this mantle. It is a reminder that David Winter is a creative artist who possesses a wealth of remarkable ideas which collectors have yet to see. In 1992 he is still only in his early thirties, and it is only twelve years since that first Mill House was sold in Guildford High Street.

Why did Cottages appeal in 1979 when heraldic plaques and Prince Charles busts did not? Probably because John Hine had identified a gap in the giftware market for quality gypsum models but had not initially discovered the theme which they should take. And what is the secret of the popularity of David Winter Cottages? The answer to this question lies in what I regard as their three main attributes.

First of all there is the base material, *Crystacal* – robust and ideal for producing finely detailed work, this is the perfect medium for Cottages and has achieved a position of respectability that plaster could never achieve.

Secondly, the use of silicon rubber moulds, a relatively new innovation, allowed for the retention of an extraordinary amount of fine detail. John Hine Studios have been a leading exponent in this field.

Thirdly, there is the emergence of a new breed of collectors – Cottage collectors – whose enthusiasm for David Winter Cottages has made them a potent influence on the giftware and collectable market in general.

Unifying all these factors is the artistic talent of David Winter himself. In 1980 he had the inherent sculpting skills and talent, but little outlet for them, and when the right subject came along it unleashed a creative flow that is still going strong well into its second decade. In the video 'Meet The Artist' John Hine sums it up admirably:

"I don't think it is possible for a large number of collectors to
follow the work of an artist unless he is an artist
of the first rank – and it's the quality of
David's work, the quality of his artistry,
that has put him where he is today."

2- HOW DAVID WINTER COTTAGES ARE MADE

David Winter sculpts his original pieces in modelling wax, generally using the handmade tools that he has devised to suit the needs of miniature work. He first 'blocks up' a piece, arranging the fundamental shapes of the buildings until they have reached a form that satisfies him. 'Blocking up' is the part David enjoys the most. Then he adds the detail, always working from top to bottom to avoid smudging the work he has already done. He finishes a piece by signing and dating the base – and by adding the mouse. (See chapter nine)

Our Master Mouldmakers receive the original wax sculpture and make a 'Gold Master' of the piece in resin. They only have one chance to get it right, as the wax is destroyed in the process! From the Gold Master come all production moulds from which David Winter Cottages are cast.

CASTING

In the Casting Department, liquid Crystacal is poured into a silicon rubber mould and rubbed by hand into all the corners to remove air bubbles and to ensure contact in every detail. Air bubbles can result in detail being lost, such as the horses' heads on **Tythe Barn**.

The mould rests in an outer case so that it doesn't distort in any way. Crystacal sets very quickly, and within half-an-hour the Cottage is ready to be demoulded.

DEMOULDING

There is considerable skill in easing the piece out of the mould. It has to be done slowly so that neither the piece nor the mould is damaged in any way (moulds are expensive and must be reused many times). If you look at a David Winter Cottage and imagine that all open spaces (archways, courtyards, crevices), have to be filled out with part of the mould, the difficulties become apparent. A good example is the alleyway through the main building on **House On Top**, which was achieved by two 'tongues' of silicon rubber that protruded from either side of the mould and met in the middle, with a slight space to create the central door.

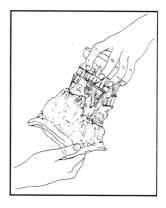

In the process of demoulding, the mould is turned

inside-out. If you look at a piece from the base viewpoint, you will see that the bulk of the piece is invisible apart from the slightest overhang of a tree or bush. This is because the pieces are demoulded base first and everything else has to squeeze through the space that it creates. Some pieces have been notoriously difficult to demould, and not necessarily complex or large ones. **Spinner's Cottage** had its own special problem because the base was not wider than the main bulk. (Turn it upside down and you will see!).

FETTLING

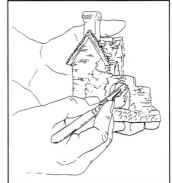

Any excess Crystacal or moulding irregularities are scraped away by hand – a process called 'fettling' (hence the expression 'to be in fine fettle'). This is commonly needed where two 'tongues' join to form archways or posts, such as those on **Tomfool's Cottage**. The tongue ends are patterned and interlock smoothly together, but a tiny ridge of Crystacal can still remain. Close inspection of pieces can sometimes detect the remains of such ridges.

PAINTING

Before being painted, all David Winter Cottages are dipped in a sealing solution, a mixture of shellac and white polish, which stops the paint being absorbed by the Crystacal.

John Hine Studios have an extensive team of painters, some working on their premises and others painting from home, often on a part-time basis. White stock is delivered to 'homepainters' in trays and painted pieces are collected at the same time and returned to the Studios for inspection and quality control. The painters follow guidelines based upon masters which, until her retirement last year, were normally (though not exclusively) originated by Audrey White, and approved by John Hine and David Winter.

Finding the master colours is not always a straightforward process. Audrey used

to paint many versions until the correct one emerged. She became so experienced at this over the years that, as Audrey herself describes, she could look at a piece and it would tell her what colours to put on!

FINISHING

Metal accessories, special paint features, baise and the backstamp are all added 'in-house' in the Finishing Department. Having been boxed with a Certificate of Authenticity, the David Winter Cottages are then despatched to shops and stores.

3 - A GUIDE TO COLLECTING DAVID WINTER COTTAGES

1 TERMINOLOGY

RETIRED — Discontinued/withdrawn/no longer made.
BACKSTAMP — Base label.
ISSUE PRICE — The first retail price at which a piece sold (or the earliest known price).
DAVID WINTER — Now used to define the Cottages as well as their sculptor.
SECONDARY MARKET — The trading of retired and early pieces between private individuals at higher-than-issue prices.

2 AUTHORISED STOCKISTS

John Hine Studios have a policy of supplying David Winter Cottages only to stockists authorised by them, and they strongly advise collectors to purchase from these stockists. Other stores and discount houses acquire their stock indirectly (a practise called "grey marketeering") and for their customers there is no recourse to John Hine Studios with regard to quality of service and additional information.

3 KEEP CERTIFICATES OF AUTHENTICITY

When you purchase a David Winter Cottage, make sure there is a Certificate of Authenticity in the box. Keep it safe, so that if you wish to sell, you can pass the Certificate on with the piece. Until recently John Hine Studios have been generous in supplying replacement Certificates (and boxes). However this policy has changed recently and replacements will be extremely difficult to get hold of in future. Keep the box, too. Even they exchange hands for a profit.

4 PURCHASE NEW PIECES EARLY

New pieces sometimes encounter problems early on, and changes in the moulds are then made to ease production. These early pieces will never be the same again and in time will become more valuable. This is particularly relevant to complex pieces, such as **CASTLE IN THE AIR**, which is already slightly different. **The Boat House** is another recent example. Early versions of pieces such as **Market Street**, **Single Oast** and **The Winemerchant** are more valuable than their re-modelled counterparts. This aspect of the secondary market is only now beginning to develop and will no doubt continue to do so as distinctions between early and late pieces emerge. The current pieces of today are the valuable sought after pieces of tomorrow.

5 PURCHASE NEWLY RETIRED PIECES WHILE YOU CAN

David Winter Cottages are retired on a regular basis. As soon as they are, they become a limited edition item and begin to appreciate in value. So if a retirement is announced, it is wise to have that piece in your collection.

Recently retired pieces can often be found in shops and stores for some time after retirement date. Although David Winter's special annual Christmas pieces are retired on 31st December of each year (with the exception of the 1987 piece, which was retired on 29th February 1988), they remain in shops and stores as long as stocks last, and it is usually possible to purchase them well into the New Year. These are worthwhile investments, as production is limited to months rather than years and therefore edition sizes are relatively low.

6 EDITION NUMBERS ARE UNKNOWN

In the early days of John Hine Studios record keeping was very patchy and no paperwork exists to give any idea of how many pieces were made. This book does not intend to speculate without evidence; nevertheless production dates can be quite revealing. Pieces such as the original **Mill House** and **Little Mill**, which were sculpted and retired within 1980 when barely a handful of people were making them, must exist in very small edition sizes. **Three Ducks Inn**, **St. Paul's Cathedral** and **Chichester Cross** were available for barely more than a year, and the **Tiny Series**, sculpted during 1980, had gone by 1982 (and in 1982 the company was still a fraction of its size ten years on). **The Provencals**, **Castle Keep**, **Double Oast** and **Sabrina's Cottage** must also be very thin on the ground, as they were listed only between 1981 and 1982 and did not sell well and John Hine would have concentrated his limited resources on producing pieces that did sell well. For example, he has said that probably no more than one hundred of Sabrina's Cottage were ever released.

Edition sizes were greater for pieces retired in 1983, and through 1984 and 1985 John Hine Studios' production capability expanded rapidly. With this in mind, plus the production dates as a guide, a proportional idea of quantities can hopefully be gleaned.

7 COLOUR VARIATIONS

Colour variations are common on David Winter Cottages as every piece is handpainted, and although painters are given a guide to follow they are allowed a certain leeway to add their own interpretation.

Early pieces had more muted colours than later ones. In fact in the 'coalshed' days the idea of selling them unpainted was considered (and rejected at the behest of stockists!). The colours have not faded over the years, as some collectors believe – this was the desired effect. It is also reasonable to suppose that when David Winter Cottages were struggling to get off the ground it was prudent to make the paint last as long as possible.

Audrey White tells us that the nature of the sculptures determines the painting style. As David Winter's technique developed, features became more prominent, more detail was added, and lines became more distinct. This demanded bolder colours and greater contrasts, plus a wider range of colours. In 1980 Audrey was using about twelve basic colours – today painters have sixty or more.

8 IDENTIFYING EARLY PIECES

There are several photographs of early and more recent pieces next to each other in this book (**Single Oast**, **Tudor Manor House**, **The Village** etc.), and they highlight several of the contrasts between them.

As mentioned already, early pieces are distinct for having muted colours. Generally speaking, early versions of pieces (current and retired) have less foliage, which is often added in the moulds as they age to reinforce sensitive areas. **Fairytale Castle** is a fine example of this.

Early pieces have hardly any flowers. **Anne Hathaway's Cottage** was the first 'David Winter' that Audrey originated with flowers; John Hine liked them and flowers began to appear regularly after that. The reds, yellows, blues and mauves used are poster paints, and not powder paint.

Early backstamps were very simple, without logos or sophisticated typefaces and were even handwritten if printed ones weren't available.

9 VARIATIONS IN DETAIL

Minor variations to detail are sometimes caused by fettling. Certain aspects of a piece such as a chimney or an archway may be smoothed or slightly altered by hand prior to painting. Far from being detrimental to the sculpture, this adds an element of individuality which is the nature of handcrafted as opposed to machine-made pieces.

Loss of detail is less of a problem today than it was on early 'David Winters'. By the end of their run, for example, **Three Ducks Inn** had lost signs off doors and **The Forge's** milestone had worn away. But contemporary moulds are sturdier; they deteriorate at a much slower rate and detail is retained longer.

10 NATIONAL TRENDS IN THE SECONDARY MARKET

By far the greatest secondary market activity takes place in North America, although the U.K. is beginning to flourish, and interest in Australia and Japan is also growing.

In North America the upper end of the market is higher than in the U.K., with prices for rare retired pieces sometimes rising beyond any reason. Yet surprisingly, the lower end is in some cases higher in the U.K. than North America, notably with recently retired pieces. This is perhaps a reflection of the U.K.'s belated awareness of the inherent value of retired 'David Winters', and possibly reflects an eagerness to acquire investments for the future.

11 FAKES

The fine detail of David Winter Cottages is virtually impossible to fake – but where there's a will there's a way, and fakes are not unknown. Only the very valuable retired pieces are worth fabricating and a small number appeared on the secondary market during 1990 and 1991, mainly of the very early retired pieces – **Provencal Two**, some of the **Tiny Series** and **Chichester Cross**. Fortunately they were not very well done and soon came to the attention of John Hine Studios, who were able to nip the problem in the bud. (A **Chichester Cross** made of Crystacal was an obvious forgery that came to light – they were only ever cast by John Hine Studios in resin.)

Paint can give the game away. Bright colours on an old piece may be suspicious, but not always: at the request of collectors, John Hine Studios have been known to repaint early pieces (although this service is no longer available.). Fakes rarely have a backstamp. It's a nuisance having to fabricate printed material as well as the piece.

Look at the baise. An old piece with fresh clean baise is a strange combination. In the event that a seller claims the piece never had baise and that it has been put on recently, peel back the baise and see if the base underneath is dirty and aged. If it isn't . . . .

'Imitation is the sincerest form of flattery', wrote the English author Charles Colton – and the fact that fakes have been discovered at all is an indication of the high standing of David Winter Cottages in the marketplace.

12 SIGNED PIECES

Like all work signed by the artist, a Cottage with David Winter's signature on it increases the inherent value appreciably. Not so long ago they were very rare indeed, but in the past few years David has made more frequent appearences at promotions throughout Europe and North America and they are now easier to acquire. But unlike other producers of similar items, David Winter does sculpt every original Cottage himself – and this demands long periods of time in his studio. The number of promotional tours he can do is limited because of this, and signed pieces will always be rare. They are well worth tracking down.

13 COLLECTORS CLUBS

Such is the popularity of David Winter Cottages that numerous regional collectors clubs now exist, mainly in the U.S.A. Their intentions vary from a desire purely to meet and converse with likeminded collectors, to the promotion of buying, selling and swapping of pieces for profit. Some clubs embrace all aspects of collecting David Winter Cottages. Similar ventures have had a checkered life in Great Britain (where collecting is perhaps more of a private activity), but there is at least one in Australia which is currently thriving.

14 BASE MARKINGS

Nowadays, all David Winter Cottages have a copyright symbol (©), the year of sculpture and David's name engraved onto the side of the base. However, most of the early pieces have none of these things, and in some cases they were added later. There are numerous variations to the markings and where known they have been listed in this book.

4 - CURRENT PIECES LISTING

Each piece was released in the same year in which it was sculpted unless stated otherwise. MARKINGS refers to information sculpted into the base (copyright symbol, signature and date) and not wording on plaques or signs on the piece.

The Heart of England Series

The Heart of England Series was first released as a ten piece set. Then The Windmill was added as number eleven after a long delay whilst a satisfactory way of making the sails was developed (it took three years!). To round it up to a dozen, an additional piece was planned but never sculpted.

THE APOTHECARY SHOP
SCULPTED: 1985
LOCATION: Home Studio
SIZE: Width: $4^{1}/8"$
Depth: 2"
Height $2^{3}/4"$
MARKINGS: © D.W.C.
1985

UPDATE: _____

BLACKFRIARS GRANGE
SCULPTED: 1985
LOCATION: Home Studio
SIZE: Width: $3^{1}/2"$
Depth: $2^{1}/8"$
Height $2^{1}/2"$
MARKINGS: © D.W.C.
1985

UPDATE: _____

CRAFTSMEN'S COTTAGES
SCULPTED: 1985
LOCATION: Home Studio
SIZE: Width: $4^{3}/4"$
Depth: $1^{7}/8"$
Height $2^{1}/2"$
MARKINGS: © D.W.C.
1985

UPDATE: _____

THE HOGS HEAD TAVERN
SCULPTED: 1985
LOCATION: Home Studio
SIZE: Width: $3^{3}/4"$
Depth: $2^{1}/8"$
Height 3"
MARKINGS: © D.W.C.
1985

UPDATE: _____

MEADOWBANK COTTAGES
SCULPTED: 1985
LOCATION: Home Studio
SIZE: Width: 4"
Depth: $1^{3}/8"$
Height $2^{1}/4"$
MARKINGS: © D.W.C.
1985

UPDATE: _____

THE SCHOOLHOUSE
SCULPTED: 1985
LOCATION: Home Studio
SIZE: Width: $3^{1}/2"$
Depth: $2^{1}/2"$
Height $2^{3}/4"$
MARKINGS: © D.W.C.
1985

UPDATE: _____

SHIREHALL

SCULPTED: 1985
LOCATION: Home Studio
SIZE: Width: 3 $^1/_2$"
Depth: 2" Height 2 $^3/_4$"
MARKINGS: © D.W.C.
1985

UPDATE: _____

ST. GEORGE'S CHURCH

SCULPTED: 1985
LOCATION: Home Studio
SIZE: Width: 4"
Depth: 2 $^1/_4$" Height 3"
MARKINGS: © D.W.C.
1985

UPDATE: _____

St George's Church is almost an exact copy of the church in the Surrey village where David Winter lives. The real church, however, is not called St. George's. There is also a very similar church at Salford in the Cotswolds.

THE VICARAGE

SCULPTED: 1985
LOCATION: Home Studio
SIZE: Width: 3 $^7/_8$"
Depth: 2 $^1/_2$" Height 3"
MARKINGS: © D.W.C.
1985

UPDATE: _____

YEOMAN'S FARMHOUSE

SCULPTED: 1985
LOCATION: Home Studio
SIZE: Width: 4 $^1/_8$"
Depth: 2" Height 2 $^1/_8$"
MARKINGS: © D.W.C.
1985

UPDATE: _____

THE WINDMILL

SCULPTED: 1985
RELEASED: 1988
LOCATION: Home Studio
SIZE: Width: 2 $^1/_4$"
Depth: 2 $^7/_8$"
Height 3 $^1/_2$"
MARKINGS: © D.W.C.
1985

UPDATE: _____

The Windmill launch was delayed for three years whilst a suitable means of making the sails was developed. The original working prototypes were made from balsa wood (though none was ever sold), then injection moulded plastic was tried but proved unsatisfactory. The eventual solution was to cast them in metal. There are numerous variations in the style of sails on early pieces as experiments were made – for example, a central cross piece with the four sails attached separately. A few early versions have only six frames on each sail, but most have seven. This is a model of a post mill, in which the circular base is fixed and the square upper body rotates in order to bring the sails into the wind.

West Country Collection

SCULPTED: 1986/7
LOCATION: Home Studio (except Orchard Cottage)

The first five pieces were sculpted in 1986 and released in 1987. Cornish Engine House and Cornish Harbour were later additions, sculpted during 1987 and launched at the same time as the Midlands Collection in 1988.

SMUGGLER'S CREEK

SIZE: Width: 7 $^1/_2$"
Depth: 5 $^1/_4$"
Height: 9"
MARKINGS: © David
Winter 1986

UPDATE: _____

Smugglers Creek is technically an extremely difficult piece to make due to the complexity of its design; this was reflected in several working names given to it by the mouldmakers, none of which are repeatable. Smugglers Creek won the 1987 award for Best Collectible of the Show at the California Plate & Collectible Show held in Pasadena.

DEVON COMBE
SIZE: Width: 5 $^7/8$"
Depth: 4 $^3/8$" Height: 5"
MARKINGS: © David
Winter 1986

UPDATE: _____

TAMAR COTTAGE
SIZE: Width: 4 $^1/2$"
Depth: 3 $^1/2$"
Height: 5"
MARKINGS: © David
Winter 1986

UPDATE: _____
Tamar Cottage is named after the river that divides Devon from Cornwall.

ORCHARD COTTAGE
SEE RETIRED PIECES LISTING.

DEVON CREAMERY
SIZE: Width: 5 $^5/8$"
Depth: 4 $^1/4$"
Height: 4 $^1/2$"
MARKINGS: © David
Winter 1986

UPDATE: _____

CORNISH ENGINE HOUSE
RELEASED: 1988
SIZE: 5 $^3/4$"
Depth: 3 $^5/8$"
Height: 7 $^1/4$"
MARKINGS: © David
Winter 1987

UPDATE: _____
The **Cornish Engine House** has a complex metal attachment – a pump wheel and connecting beam that actually turns. The balcony is also metal.

CORNISH HARBOUR
RELEASED: 1988
SIZE: Width: 5 $^3/4$"
Depth: 5 $^1/2$"
Height: 6 $^1/4$"
MARKINGS: © David
Winter 1987

UPDATE: _____

The Midlands Collection

SCULPTED: 1987
LOCATION: Home Studio
RELEASED: 1988

LOCK-KEEPER'S COTTAGE
SIZE: Width: 5"
Depth: 4 $^1/2$"
Height: 3 $^1/4$"
MARKINGS: © David
Winter 1987

UPDATE: _____
The barrel-shaped roof of **Lock-Keeper's Cottage** is unique to a ten-mile stretch of canal to the north of Stratford-Upon-Avon, Warwickshire, where several examples can still be seen today. However, David's piece is not a model of any one in particular; he used photographs as a guide and let his imagination do the rest.

BOTTLE KILN
SEE RETIRED PIECES LISTING.

DERBYSHIRE COTTON MILL
SIZE: Width: 7"
Depth: 4"
Height: 8 $^1/_2$"
MARKINGS: © David
Winter 1987

UPDATE: _____
Derbyshire Cotton Mill is a reworking of David's earlier Cotton Mill sculpted in 1983. The mill building has been extended, brick ridges added to the chimney stack, and the footbridge is an entirely new feature.

GUNSMITHS
SIZE: Width: 4"
Depth: 3 $^1/_2$"
Height: 4 $^3/_4$"
MARKINGS: © David
Winter 1987

UPDATE: _____
The Aston district of Birmingham was its gunsmiths' quarter, and there are still traditional craftsmen at work there. Their premises are entirely functional and not at all pleasing to the eye, so David Winter had carte blanche to make of **The Gunsmiths** piece anything that he wished.

LACEMAKERS
SIZE: Width: 4 $^1/_4$"
Depth: 4 $^3/_4$"
Height: 6"
MARKINGS: © David
Winter 1987

UPDATE: _____
Lacemakers is a favourite piece of many collectors. David Winter himself once said that he wouldn't mind living there. The metal bannister down the steps is an awkward feature to fit, and the piece was widely tipped for retirement in the autumn of 1991. Originally called Lacemakers Cottage, but 'Cottage', was soon dropped.

COALMINERS ROW
SIZE: Width: 6 $^3/_4$"
Depth: 4"
Height: 4 $^1/_4$"
MARKINGS: © David
Winter 1987

UPDATE: _____
Coalminers Row is usually abbreviated to Miners Row on base labels, certificates of authenticity, promotional material etc., although the piece was officially launched as Coalminers Row (or Coal Miners Row).

The Scottish Collection

SCULPTED: 1988 (except Scottish Crofters)
LOCATION: Home Studio
RELEASED: 1989 (except The Old Distillery. See also remarks about Scottish Crofters)

THE HOUSE ON THE LOCH
SIZE: Width: 4 $^5/_8$"
Depth: 4 $^1/_2$"
Height: 4"
MARKINGS: © David
Winter 1988

UPDATE: _____
Watch out for Nessie peeping out of the murky waters of the **House on the loch**. This is the only David Winter Cottage to feature a monster.

MACBETH'S CASTLE
SIZE: Width: 5 $^1/_2$"
Depth: 4 $^1/_2$"
Height: 8 $^1/_2$"
MARKINGS: © David
Winter 1988

UPDATE: _____

David consulted photographs and illustrations of various Scottish castles whilst sculpting **Macbeth's Castle**, including Cawdor Castle, near Inverness. (In Shakespeare's play Macbeth becomes Thane of Cawdor.) Nevertheless this is an imaginary piece, and the inspiration behind it reflects the real Macbeth (King of Scotland from AD 1040 to 1057) who was a benevolent and well-respected leader, and not Shakespeare's evil character.

GILLIE'S COTTAGE

SIZE: Width: 5"
Depth: 4"
Height: 4 $^1/_4$"
MARKINGS: © David Winter 1988

UPDATE: _____

GATEKEEPERS

SIZE: Width: 4 $^1/_4$"
Depth: 3 $^1/_8$"
Height: 5 $^1/_4$"
MARKINGS: © David Winter 1988

UPDATE: _____

SCOTTISH CROFTERS

SIZE: Width: 5"
Depth: 3 $^1/_2$"
Height: 4 $^3/_4$"
MARKINGS: © David Winter 1986

UPDATE: _____

The stone weights held by rope onto the thatch are the only feature that make Scottish Crofters different from Crofters Cottage. The piece was going to keep the same name, but it began to be called Scottish Crofters at John Hine Studios to distinguish it from the original – and the name stuck. The original was sculpted at 19 Ash Street and the stone weights were added at Home Studio. Scottish Crofters retains the same date on the base as Crofters Cottage.

THE OLD DISTILLERY

SIZE: Width: 10 $^1/_4$"
Depth: 7 $^1/_2$"
Height: 9 $^1/_4$"
MARKINGS: © David Winter 1982

UPDATE: _____

The Old Distillery was sculpted at Hendon Road and launched in 1982, then relaunched as part of the Scottish Collection in 1989. Meanwhile, in 1986, various changes were made to the piece.
* Foliage was added to the middle of the group of buildings on the right side.
* The roof of the largest building in the left side grouping was tapered at the back to prevent demoulding damage.
* The front extension to the large building between the two chimney stacks was shortened by half-an-inch, again to ease demoulding. The new area in front of it was remodelled and new crates added.
No further changes (apart from the base label) were made when The Old Distillery joined The Scottish Collection, although the word 'old' seems to have been dropped and the piece is more often described as The Distillery.

BRITISH TRADITIONS COLLECTION

Twelve pieces reflecting great British traditions – one for each month of the year.
SCULPTED: 1989
LOCATION: Home Studio
RELEASED: 1990

BURNS' READING ROOM

SIZE: Width: 3 $^1/_4$"
Depth: 2"
Height: 3 $^1/_4$"
MARKINGS: © D.W.C. 1989

UPDATE: _____

JANUARY. **Burns' Reading Room** is inspired by Burns' Night (25th January) and specifically by a painting – William Smellie's Printing Office, Anchor Close, Edinburgh by Henry G. Duiguid – which can be seen in the Prints & Drawing Room of the National Gallery of Scotland, Edinburgh. (William Smellie was the publisher of some of Robert Burns' poetry.)

STONECUTTER'S COTTAGE
SIZE: Width: 4 $^1/_2$"
Depth: 3 $^1/_4$"
Height: 4 $^1/_2$"
MARKINGS: © D.W.C.
1989

UPDATE: _____

FEBRUARY. **The Stonecutter's Cottage** is inspired by the Annual Meeting of the Ancient Order of Purbeck Marblers and Stonecutters, held on Shrove Tuesday at the Town Hall, Corfe Castle, Dorset.

THE BOAT HOUSE
SIZE: Width: 3 $^7/_8$"
Depth: 2 $^3/_4$"
Height: 4 $^3/_8$"
MARKINGS: © D.W.C.
1989

UPDATE: _____

MARCH. **The Boat House** is inspired by the Oxford and Cambridge Boat Race. The position of the shim (the cut in the mould necessary for removing the piece) around the front post was altered several times from a diagonal to a vertical cut. On the models all this meant was that the slight ridge this sometimes leaves on the stone floor was in a different position. There are also variations on the top row of chimney bricks. Some are well defined, others are bevelled from the outer edge down to the chimney.

PUDDING COTTAGE
SIZE: Width: 3 $^5/_8$"
Depth: 3 $^3/_8$"
Height: 5 $^1/_4$"
MARKINGS: © D.W.C.
1989

UPDATE: _____

APRIL: **Pudding Cottage** – Home of Yorkshire Pudding Bushes? Squire Reginald Chuckerbuttie and his pet dog Sprout?? The Addlethwaite Yorkshire Pudding Festival??? The launch story in the Summer '89 issue of Cottage Country might just have been credible had the Festival not taken place on 1st April! Pudding Cottage is of course an April Fool!

BLOSSOM COTTAGE
SIZE: Width: 4"
Depth: 3 $^5/_8$"
Height: 4 $^1/_2$"
MARKINGS: © D.W.C.
1989

UPDATE: _____

MAY. **Blossom Cottage** was inspired by the Chelsea Flower Show.

KNIGHT'S CASTLE
SIZE: Width: 3 $^3/_8$"
Depth: 3 $^1/_4$"
Height: 6"

UPDATE: _____

JUNE. **Knight's Castle** was inspired by the Garter Day Ceremony held at Windsor Castle.

ST. ANNE'S WELL
SIZE: Width: 4 $^1/_4$"
Depth: 3 $^1/_4$"
Height: 4 $^5/_8$"

UPDATE: _____

JULY. **St Anne's Well** was inspired by the ancient custom of Well Dressing, a traditional almost unique to Derbyshire these days. St. Anne is the Patron Saint of wells.

GROUSE MOOR LODGE
SIZE: Width: 3 $^1/_8$"
Depth: 2 $^7/_8$"
Height: 4 $^3/_4$"
MARKINGS: © D.W.C.
1989

UPDATE: _____
AUGUST. **Grouse Moor Lodge** was inspired by the start of the grouse shooting season – 12th August – better known as the Glorious Twelfth.

STAFFORDSHIRE VICARAGE
SIZE: Width: 4 $^1/_4$"
Depth: 3" Height: 4"
MARKINGS: © D.W.C.
1989

UPDATE: _____
SEPTEMBER. **Staffordshire Vicarage** was inspired by the Abbots Bromley Horn Dance, a thousand year old Staffordshire custom which begins with a dance on the vicarage lawn.

HARVEST BARN
SIZE: Width: 4"
Depth: 2 $^1/_2$"
Height: 2 $^1/_2$"
MARKINGS: © D.W.C.
1989

UPDATE: _____
OCTOBER. **Harvest Barn** was inspired by the Harvest Festival church service.

GUY FAWKES
SIZE: Width: 2 $^3/_4$"
Depth: 2 $^1/_2$"
Height: 3 $^1/_4$"
MARKINGS: © D.W.C.
1989

UPDATE: _____
NOVEMBER. **Guy Fawkes** took inspiration from the notorious Gunpowder Plot of 1605 and its annual celebration on 5th November. – Bonfire Night.

THE BULL AND BUSH
SIZE: Width: 4 $^1/_8$"
Depth: 2 $^1/_2$"
Height: 4"
MARKINGS: © D.W.C.
1989

UPDATE: _____
DECEMBER. **The Bull and Bush** was inspired by the tradition of pantomime and the roots of its great performers in the pubs and music halls of Britain.

Pieces Not in Series or Collections

THE BAKE HOUSE
SCULPTED: 1983
LOCATION: Home Studio
MARKINGS: © David
Winter 1983
SIZE: Width: 3 $^1/_2$
Depth: 2 $^3/_4$"
Height 4"

UPDATE: _____
Very early models of **The Bakehouse** (made in 1983) have one less band of bricks on the chimney.

BOOKENDS (The Printers/The Bookbinders)

SCULPTED: 1989
RELEASED: 1991
LOCATION: Home Studio
SIZE: THE PRINTERS: Width: 3"
Depth: 2 $^3/_4$"
Height 4 $^3/_4$"
SIZE: THE BOOKBINDERS:
SIZE: Width: 3 $^1/_8$"
Depth: 2 $^3/_4$"
Height: 4 $^3/_4$"
MARKINGS: © D.W.C. 1989

UPDATE: _____
When **Bookends** were first sculpted, they did not have the weight to hold ordinary books in place; they kept slipping over. So John Hine decided to publish some books to match their size, and the launch was postponed whilst the books were in production. Eventually the twelve British Traditions books materialised and were launched with the Bookends. The Printers and The Bookbinders can only be purchased as a pair, but the British Traditions books are available individually or as a set.
Bookends were also at one stage considered as a special Guild item.

THE BOTHY
SCULPTED: 1983
LOCATION: Home Studio
SIZE: Width: 4"
Depth: 3 $^1/_8$"
Height 3 $^5/_8$"
MARKINGS: © David
Winter 1983

UPDATE: _____

CASTLE GATE
SCULPTED: 1984
LOCATION: Hendon Rd
SIZE: Width: 7"
Depth: 5" Height 8 $^3/_8$"
MARKINGS: © David
Winter 1984

UPDATE: _Retired Feb 1992!_
In the set of David Winter Cards, there is an interesting photograph of David at work sculpting **Castle Gate.** The version he is working on varies considerably from the finished piece. Apparently this is because he actually sculpted a complete castle façade and then crumbled it away to give a ruined look. The cottages built from the castle stones were added afterwards. However, all these changes occurred during sculpting, and no alterations were made during production. David is very fond of Castle Gate.

CASTLE IN THE AIR
SCULPTED: 1991
LOCATION: Home Studio
SIZE: Width: 6 $^5/_8$"
Depth: 5 $^5/_8$" Height 11"
MARKINGS: © David
Winter 1991

UPDATE: _____
A complex piece such as **CASTLE IN THE AIR** is bound to alter in the course of time. The points where the metal flags are attached to the piece have already been reinforced with metal supports. CASTLE IN THE AIR was originally supplied with two metal cannons, but it is currently being supplied with three.

THE CHAPEL
SCULPTED: 1984
LOCATION: 19 Ash St
(on the kitchen table)
SIZE: Width: 4 $^1/_2$"
Depth: 3 $^5/_8$"
Height 5 $^3/_4$"
MARKINGS: © David
Winter 1984

UPDATE: _____

THE COOPER'S COTTAGE
SCULPTED: 1985
LOCATION: 19 Ash Street
SIZE: Width: 3"
Depth: 3 $^1/_2$"
Height: 4 $^1/_2$"
MARKINGS: © David
Winter 1985

UPDATE: _____

COTSWOLD COTTAGE
SCULPTED: 1982
LOCATION: Hendon
Road
SIZE: Width: 2 $^3/_4$"
Depth: 2 $^1/_2$"
Height 2 $^1/_8$"
MARKINGS: © David
Winter 1982

UPDATE: _____
Early models of **Cotswold Cottage** (during first
year of production) have more prominent
overhangs on the end gables and porchway.
These were shortened to ease demoulding.

THE DOWER HOUSE
SCULPTED: 1982
LOCATION: Hendon
Road
SIZE: Width 3 1/4" Depth:
2" Height: 2 1/2"
MARKINGS: © David
Winter 1982

UPDATE: _____

DROVER'S COTTAGE
SCULPTED: 1982
LOCATION: Hendon
Road
SIZE: Width: 3 $^1/_8$"
Depth: 1 $^7/_8$"
Height 2 $^3/_8$"
MARKINGS: © David
Winter 1982

UPDATE: _____

FISHERMAN'S WHARF
SCULPTED: 1983
LOCATION: Hendon
Road
Width: 4 $^1/_2$"
Depth: 3 $^1/_8$"
Height: 3 $^3/_4$"
MARKINGS: © David
Winter 1983

UPDATE: _____
Early models of **Fisherman's Wharf** have less
greenery, especially growing up to raised gable
ends.

THE GREEN DRAGON INN
SCULPTED: 1983
LOCATION: Hendon
Road
SIZE: Width: 4 $^1/_2$"
Depth: 3 $^3/_8$"
Height 3 $^1/_2$"
MARKINGS: © David
Winter 1983

UPDATE: _____
Very early models of **The Green Dragon Inn** do not
have the foliage arch at the top of the stairs.
Other than that, the main changes have been to
the pub sign. Today it is made of metal with the
sign etched onto it, but this has been preceded
by brown and black plastic ones, both with a
paper label sign. To accommodate the metal
sign, the bushes around its base were extended.
The name of this piece has been corrupted over
the years into the **Green Dragon Pub**, an error into
which even John Hine Studios have lapsed!
However, the Green Dragon Inn is its original and
proper name.

HERTFORD COURT
SCULPTED: 1983
LOCATION: Home Studio
SIZE: Width: 5 $^1/_2$"
Depth: 3 $^3/_4$"
Height 5 $^3/_4$"
MARKINGS: © David
Winter 1983

UPDATE: _____
A very small number of **Hertford Court** at the
beginning of production were made with a
smaller courtyard and centre section of the main

building, and much less foliage generally. Examples of this original version are very rare. The courtyard was widened to ease demoulding; prior to the change the balcony on the right side tended to be pulled off with the mould. There were some production problems with this piece during 1990 and it was widely tipped to be retired, but it is currently still going strong. Until properly titled, Hertford Court was given the working name of 'Eric', and John Hine still thinks of it as such to this day.

INGLENOOK COTTAGE

SCULPTED: 1991
LOCATION: Home Studio
SIZE: Width: 3 $^1/_2$"
Depth: 3 $^5/_8$" Height: 5"
MARKINGS: © David
Winter 1991

UPDATE:
The metal gate is an interesting feature on **Inglenook Cottage**. This, together with CASTLE IN THE AIR demonstrates that despite problems with metal accessories in the past, John Hine Studios are still prepared to experiment and try new ideas.

IVY COTTAGE

SCULPTED: 1982
LOCATION: 19 Ash Street
SIZE: Width: 3 $^1/_2$"
Depth: 2 $^1/_2$"
Height 3 $^1/_2$"
MARKINGS: David
Winter/c David Winter
1982

UPDATE:
Very early models of **Ivy Cottage** were slightly taller than the main production run; the shorter version developed soon after Ivy Cottage was launched. Early models are also missing the white stepping stones at the front and right side. and the flower boxes (these pieces are not dated). More ivy was added when these modifications were made in 1983. It spread onto the roof at one stage but has now disappeared again!

JOHN BENBOW'S FARMHOUSE

SCULPTED: 1987
LOCATION: Home Studio
SIZE: Width: 5"
Depth: 4 $^3/_8$"
Height 3 $^3/_4$"
MARKINGS: © David
Winter 1987

UPDATE:
By 1987 David Winter had stopped sculpting existing buildings entirely, but **John Benbow's Farmhouse** is an exception with this model of Hill Farm near Ledbury, Herefordshire. It is the home of John Benbow. He worked and lived on this farm when he was visited by American missionary Wilford Woodruff who baptised him and encouraged him to join the Mormon community in Salt Lake City, Utah. The piece was sculpted at the request of a stockist, Raffles in Windsor, Berkshire, who in turn received the suggestion from some of their numerous Mormon customers. John Benbow's Farmhouse was available exclusively from Raffles for a year, and it was not intended to include it in the main Collection. Popular demand persuaded John Hine Studios otherwise. The piece is dedicated to the memory of John Benbow and helped to commemorate the 150th anniversary of the British Mission of the Church of Jesus Christ of Latter-day Saints. This was the first David Winter Cottage to have a metal accessory – the 'timber' supports to the porch.
The pieces sold exclusively for Raffles had a customised backstamp.
(David has sculpted one other real building since – Wintershill for the Jim'll Fix It show)

KENT COTTAGE

SCULPTED: 1985
LOCATION: Faith
Winter's Studio
Width: 6 $^3/_8$"
Depth: 3 $^1/_2$"
Height: 4 $^1/_8$"
MKGS: © David Winter
1985

UPDATE:
Inspiration for **Kent Cottage** came from a dilapidated old house that David Winter came across once and almost drove right past. He stopped, photographed it and used his picture as

the basis of the piece. Unfortunately neither David nor Jonno Suart (who was with him at the time) can remember its precise location, other than "somewhere in Kent". It may have been in the Deal/Folkestone area.

LITTLE MARKET
SCULPTED: 1980
LOCATION:
(orig) The Coalshed
(remod) Hendon Road
SIZE: Width: 3 $^1/_4$"
Depth: 3 $^1/_8$" Height: 3"
MARKINGS: (orig) ©
David Winter 1980;
(remod) David Winter/
© David Winter 1983

UPDATE: _____
David cleverly divided Market Street into two and created a new piece from each of the halves. **Little Market** is the right half, and The Winemerchant is the left. The join side of Little Market was resculpted to include an additional covered stall. The original Little Mill had a name plaque and was named and dated 1980; during remodelling the plaque was removed and the date changed to 1983, although some pieces also exist without any date. No explanation for this has yet been discovered. Otherwise, Little Market is very similar to its Market Street original. Alterations during restyling were exactly as on Market Street.

MARKET STREET
SCULPTED: 1980
(remodelled 1983)
LOCATION: The
Coalshed (original) and
remodelled at Hendon
Road.
SIZE: Width: 5 $^1/_2$"
Depth: 4" Height: 4 $^1/_2$"
MARKINGS: (original)
None; (restyled) ©
David Winter 1980

UPDATE: _____
Market Street is one of only four pieces still available that were made in 1980, the first year of David Winter Cottages (the others are Little Market, The Winemerchant and Rose Cottage). Although it was remodelled in 1983 because of

major deterioration to the production moulds, the piece has not changed fundamentally, and alterations were to specific detail. There was no name or date on the original, and when it was added during remodelling, the original date – 1980 – was used.

ORIGINAL	REMODELLED
No name or date.	Name and date added.
Chimneys smaller and lower.	Chimneys larger, squarer, and rising above roof level.
Back door has horizontal and diagonal cross bars.	Back door has no cross bars.
Cellar window at front not very distinct.	Cellar door enlarged and more defined.
Crest of back roof to right overlaps front roof	Front roof is higher than back roof.
No foliage.	Foliage added in a variety of places.

Other changes include:
* Changes to the patterns of beam work.
* Restyling of all windows (especially second from right front, which becomes much crisper).
* The lower window at left rear is higher on the remodelled version.

MOONLIGHT HAVEN
SCULPTED: 1991
LOCATION: Home Studio
SIZE: Width: 5 $^5/_8$"
Depth: 5 $^1/_2$"
Height 5 $^1/_2$"
MARKINGS.: © David
Winter 1991

UPDATE: _____
The working title for **Moonlight Haven** was Piano Cottage as there is a piano to be found on the outside terrace. It was originally intended to be special Guild piece Number Ten; then the decision was made to include it in the main Collection instead and the Guild inscription was removed from the base. The piece was made soon after John Hine's music had been recorded for the soundtrack of the *Meet The Artist* video, and this was fresh in David's mind whilst working on it. He also sculpted the piano "to give John something to write about!"

THE PARSONAGE

SCULPTED: 1984
(remodelled 1986)
LOCATION: David's
parents' house.
SIZE: Width: 9 $^1/2$"
Depth: 7 $^1/4$" Height: 9"
MARKINGS: © David
Winter 1984

UPDATE:

In 1984 David Winter stopped working at Hendon Road and decided to set up his own studio at home. In the interim period he sculpted **The Parsonage** in a bedroom at his parents' house. By the time he came to make revisions two years later, he was able to do them in his newly converted Home Studio. Two main features distinguish the original from the remodelled version of The Parsonage:

* The original has a slightly smaller courtyard with the weather boarded building on the front right set further in. The building was moved about half-an-inch to the right to make demoulding easier.

* The walls of the porch are more extended on the original. They have been pulled back as they were easily broken.

PILGRIM'S REST

SCULPTED: 1983
LOCATION: Parents'
home (after Hendon
Road and before
setting up Home Studio)
SIZE: Width: 4"
Depth: 4" Height: 4 $^1/8$"
MARKINGS: © David
Winter 1983

UPDATE:

Pilgrim's Rest is an interesting piece for David Winter to have sculpted as he actually lives on the Pilgrims Way, the traditional route followed by pilgrims making the journey from Winchester to Canterbury to pay homage at the tomb of murdered Archbishop of Canterbury Thomas Becket.

ROSE COTTAGE

SCULPTED: 1980
(remodelled 1983)
LOCATION: The
Coalshed (remodelled
at Hendon Road)
SIZE: Width: 4 $^1/2$"
Depth: 3" Height: 2 $^3/4$"
MARKINGS: © David
Winter 1980

UPDATE:

One of the earliest David Winter Cottages still available, **Rose Cottage** was remodelled in 1983 when moulds lost their detail. White circular paving stones were added to the pathway and the thatch and porch detail were given more definition.

SINGLE OAST

SCULPTED: 1981
(remodelled 1985)
LOCATION: 19 Ash Street
SIZE: Width: 4"
Depth: 2 $^3/4$"
Height 4 $^1/2$"
MARKINGS: (original)
David Winter;
(remodelled) © David
Winter 1985

UPDATE:

With Double and Triple Oast, **Single Oast** was one of the first pieces made after the move to Ash Street. The original has David's signature but no date on the base and when it was remodelled in 1985 the remodelling date was added and not 1981. By then it had shrunk by half-an-inch (actual dimensions: 3 $^1/2$" Depth: 2 $^1/4$" Height 4") due to gradual contraction of the moulds. The open side door stands out from the wall of the current model, but on the original it lay flat against the wall. The original was devoid of all foliage and had no white fence at the front.

The wind vanes on a very small number of Oast pieces were made of Crystacal and were easily broken. They soon changed to a resin composite. In 1986 they changed again to metal and are currently made of plastic. The white peaks (cowls) were modified slightly in the process, to accommodate the new vanes.

Single and Triple Oasts with the original Crystacal vanes intact are very rare indeed.

Colour variations: early pieces had dark grey roofs, but most have the current reddish tile colour (see picture of Double Oast).

SNOW COTTAGE

SCULPTED: 1984
LOCATION: Hendon Road
SIZE: Width: 5"
Depth: 4 $^1/4$"
Height 5 $^1/2$"
MARKINGS: © David Winter 1984

UPDATE: _____

Snow Cottage was originally entitled 'Christmas Cottage', and a few of the early pieces were sold with that name on the label before the name Snow Cottage was finalised. The change was made so that the piece could be bought all year round and not just at Christmas. On the snow-covered roof there are patches where the tiles show through. These were left unpainted on some models, where painters didn't appreciate the effect required.

STRATFORD HOUSE

SCULPTED: 1981
LOCATION: 19 Ash Street
SIZE: Width: 6 $^1/4$"
Depth: 4" Height 4 $^5/8$"
MARKINGS: David Winter

UPDATE: _____

Stratford House has David's signature but no date on the base. Early pieces have a gap between the main building and the small house at the left front. They were then joined by an arch of greenery to help solve casting problems, and on later models the arch was filled in completely. The section protruding from the upper floor at the back is an early example of an indoor lavatory – a feature unique to this piece!
Stratford House is a very important piece to David; it is regarded by him as the piece that established the distinctive style of David Winter Cottages. It took him a long time to "get it right", and when he finally did, he felt strongly that his technique in sculpting miniature cottages had reached maturity.

SUSSEX COTTAGE

SCULPTED: 1982
LOCATION: Hendon Road
SIZE: Width: 3 $^1/2$"
Depth: 2 $^1/4$"
Height 2 $^1/2$"
MARKINGS: © David Winter 1982

UPDATE: _____

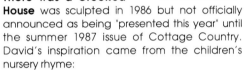

THERE WAS A CROOKED HOUSE

SCULPTED: 1986
LOCATION: Home Studio
SIZE: Width: 4"
Depth: 4 $^1/4$"
Height 7 $^1/8$"
MARKINGS: © David Winter 1987

UPDATE: _____

There was a Crooked House was sculpted in 1986 but not officially announced as being "presented this year" until the summer 1987 issue of Cottage Country. David's inspiration came from the children's nursery rhyme:
There was a crooked man and he walked a crooked mile,
He found a crooked sixpence against a crooked stile;
He bought a crooked cat, which caught a crooked mouse,
And they all lived together in a little crooked house.
The sixpence, the stile, the cat and the mouse (of course!) all feature on the sculpture. This is probably the easiest mouse to find on all David Winter Cottages. The cat is looking straight at it!
A feature unique to this model is that it has outside plumbing; there is a drainpipe down the left side. Colour variations exist. The triangular sections on the conical roof were pale green on earlier models, but they are more commonly grey.
This is Audrey White's favourite piece.

TOLLKEEPER'S COTTAGE

SCULPTED: 1983
RELEASED: 1984
LOCATION: Hendon Rd
SIZE: W: 5" D: 3 $^7/_8$"
Height 6"
MARKINGS: © David
Winter 1983

UPDATE: _____
Very early models of **Tollkeeper's Cottage** have less foliage generally; it was added during the first year of production. A picture of Tollkeeper's Cottage in the Spring 1989 issue of *Cottage Country* caused erroneous speculation that David Winter had made a curious remodelling of the piece. The photograph had been printed in reverse!

TRIPLE OAST

SCULPTED: 1981
(remodelled 1985)
LOCATION: 19 Ash
Street (one of the first
pieces made there)
SIZE: Width: 7 $^1/_4$"
Depth: 4 $^5/_8$"
Height 5 $^1/_2$"
MARKINGS: © David
Winter

UPDATE: _____
Triple Oast was restyled in 1985 along the same lines as Single Oast, with more foliage and white fences added. Early pieces had dark grey roofs, but a reddish tile colour is the norm. The original and the remodelled Triple Oast just have David's name on the base, unlike Single Oast on which the date was added during remodelling.

THE VILLAGE

SCULPTED: 1981
(remodelled 1986)
LOCATION: 19 Ash
Street (remodelled at
Hendon Road).
SIZE: Width: 12 $^1/_4$"
Depth: 8" Height: 7 $^1/_4$"
MARKINGS: © David
Winter 1981

UPDATE: _____

Originally launched as a special piece for Christmas 1981, **The Village** took three months to sculpt. It was out of production for eight months in 1986 whilst restyling took place in order to make casting and demoulding easier. The main differences between the original Village and the remodelled version are as follows:
* The building at the left front of the piece, in front of the courtyard, was shortened by about half-an-inch, with appropriate remodelling to the end of the building and the courtyard itself.
* On the right side of the piece, a buttress was removed from the side of the stone archway.
* The rear of the tall stone building at the front of the piece was cut back flush with its chimney and covered over with foliage. (This same chimney has an unusual shape, like a pyramid without a top, which was how David sculpted it originally. However, it was changed early on to a simpler design to ease demoulding, but was changed back again in 1983.)
* Arches of foliage were added in various places, linking buildings together, to help the moulds keep their shape. More foliage was added generally, too.
Colour variations on The Village are common, especially on the early pieces. This is because when the piece first appeared, the best painters John Hine had at the time were given an entirely free hand to interpret it how they wished. Different types of paints were also being experimented with at the time.
In the first two years of production, pieces became gradually narrower along the length as moulds distorted, but this was corrected in 1983.

THE VILLAGE SHOP

SCULPTED: 1982
LOCATION: Hendon
Road
SIZE: Width: 2 $^7/_8$"
Depth: 2" Height: 2 $^3/_4$"
MARKINGS: © David
Winter © David Winter
1983

UPDATE: _____
The name on the **Village Shop** sign is a pun. Only someone called Askew could live in a building that is so "askew". Some early models have no date whilst others have the wrong date – 1983!

THE WEAVER'S LODGINGS

SCULPTED: 1991
LOCATION: Home Studio
SIZE: Width: 3 $^3/_4$"
Depth: 3 $^3/_8$"
Height 4 $^7/_8$"
MARKINGS: © David
Winter 1991

UPDATE: _____

The Weaver's Lodgings has a metal balcony, which is very delicate and has been known to fall off. This may see alterations at some stage.

THE WINEMERCHANT

SCULPTED: 1980
(remodelled 1983)
LOCATION: The
Coalshed (original),
then remodelled at
Hendon Road.
SIZE: Width: 3 $^1/_2$"
Depth: 2 $^1/_2$"
Height 4 $^1/_8$"
MARKINGS: © David Winter 1980

UPDATE: _____

Like Little Mill, **The Winemerchant** derives from half of the original Market Street, with no major changes – apart from adding a chimney to the right side where the two halves joined. The original had no name and no date on the base, but both were added during remodelling in 1983, which was necessary due to loss of detail in the moulds.

Changes are similar to those made on Market Street:

* The original chimneys are shorter and squatter.
* Beams across the front of the piece were replaced by weather boarding (although David Winter states that his initial sculpture did have the weatherboarding, and some very early pieces like this may exist).
* Foliage was added in various places, notably to the right front side and along the back wall.
* The wording on the shop sign changed in style.
* The original back door had horizontal and diagonal cross bars which disappeared during remodelling.
* Windows were reshaped.

The name on the winemerchant's sign, Fred'k Venzer, is a thinly disguised variation of Frederick Winter, which happens to be David's father's name.

5 - A NOTE ABOUT PRICES

John Hine Studios have for some years maintained a policy of non-involvement with the secondary market, and although I have compiled the secondary market prices to be found in this book, I must point out that the information has been gleaned entirely from sources outside John Hine Studios – from dealers and collectors.

The secondary market in David Winter Cottages is still in its infancy compared to many (*most!*) other collectables, and I have found that the price range of retired pieces varies considerably depending on the source. So in these cases I have taken a middle line, selecting an average price band from the information available. In contrast, if individual sales of rarer pieces are the only source available, these have been quoted precisely.

It must be stressed that the prices quoted in this book are intended as a guide only. The secondary market is an ever-fluctuating beast! A piece is only worth what the buyer is willing to pay and a seller is willing to accept. It is these fluctuations in prices – and being aware of them – which makes collecting so much fun. A small space marked *Update* has been left next to the details of most Cottages in this book in which new information about prices can be jotted down.

Another important point for collectors to note is that when selling to a dealer they should be prepared to deduct up to 40% from the market price.

Issue prices for the UK are based on original price lists in John Hine Studios' archives, dating back to the very first sale in March 1980, and are accurate to the nearest fifty pence.

Bargain hunting is as enjoyable and important a part of acquiring David Winter Cottages as any other collectable. But it should be remembered that ultimately a 'bargain' is not a piece that is purchased for less than it is worth – it is a piece that has been purchased for less than you were prepared to pay.

6 - RETIRED PIECES LISTING

The U.S. issue price of certain pieces is not available because those pieces were retired before David Winter Cottages were marketed in North America. Other prices are not available because there is no known track record from which to quote. (N/A = Not Available)

Each piece was launched in the same year it was sculpted unless stated otherwise.

MARKINGS refers to information sculpted into the base (copyright symbol, signature and date) and not wording on plaques or signs on the piece.

THE ALMS HOUSES
SCULPTED: 1983
LOCATION: Faith Winter's studio
RETIRED: 1987
SIZE: Width: 7" Depth: 4 $^3/_8$" Height 4 $^1/_4$"
The stone walls on early models are less sturdy than later ones, and prior to 1984 the gutters were deeper.

There is a similarity between the gabled facade of The Alms Houses and that of the Hogs Back Hotel, near Farnham, Surrey, which is not far from David Winter's home. Although no deliberate connection was intended, David Winter admits it may have influenced him subconsciously.

The spheres on either side of the gables are attached with the barest amount of Crystacal and are very delicate.

MARKINGS: © David Winter 1983

ISSUE PRICE:	£22	$60
CURRENT VALUE:	£250 – 400	$500 – 750
UPDATE:		

BLACKSMITH'S COTTAGE
SCULPTED: 1982
LOCATION: Hendon Road
RETIRED: 1986
SIZE: Width: 4 $^1/_8$" Depth: 2" Height 2"
The decision to retire this piece was made in 1985; however, some were still leaving John Hine Limited workshops in early 1986 as existing stocks diminished. Some were painted with grey walls and black slate roofs, whilst others were severely black all over.

MARKINGS: David Winter

ISSUE PRICE:	£6	$22
CURRENT VALUE:	£125 – 175	$450 – 650
UPDATE:		

BOTTLE KILN
SCULPTED: 1987
LOCATION: Home Studio
RETIRED: Nov 1991
SIZE: Width: 6 $^3/_4$" Depth: 4 $^3/_4$" Height: 4 $^1/_2$"
Bottle Kiln is based partly on the Gladstone Pottery Museum, Stoke-On-Trent, which David Winter visited whilst researching the Midlands Collection. The piece was originally referred to in the plural (Bottle Kilns), but the 's' has gradually been dropped. In one of those little rooms clustered around the central courtyard worked the "saggar makers' bottom knocker"; but that's another story!

MARKINGS: © David Winter 1987

ISSUE PRICE:	£28	$78
CURRENT PRICE:	£45 – 50	$85 – 90
UPDATE:		

BROOKSIDE HAMLET
SCULPTED: 1982
LOCATION: Hendon Road
RETIRED: April 1991
SIZE: Width: 6 $^1/_2$" Depth: 4 $^5/_8$" Height 4 $^3/_4$"
The first piece sculpted by David Winter at the Hendon Road premises. Early pieces have hardly any water dripping from the water wheel, a deeper hollow above the wheel, no greenery behind it (on the corner of the mill building), and less greenery on corners generally. There was originally a recess next to the door of the building at the top right; to ease demoulding, this was filled in with greenery. These changes were made gradually throughout 1984 and 1985, and Brookside Hamlet remained standard until it was retired in April 1991.

This piece is featured in the small Collectors' Book/Catalogue in a short story called 'Brookside Halmet – a Fable', and is accompanied by a set of fascinating line drawings of how the hamlet might have developed.

Like The Village Shop, mystery surrounds the fact that this piece was released in 1982 and yet its base marking is 1983. Some early pieces are not dated at all.

MARKINGS: David Winter/ © David Winter 1983

ISSUE PRICE:	£23	$75
CURRENT VALUE:	£50 – 60	$100 – 130
UPDATE:		

CASTLE KEEP

SCULPTED: 1981
LOCATION: 19 Ash Street
RETIRED: 1982
SIZE: Width: 3 ^{1}/$_2$" Depth: 3 ^{3}/$_4$" Height 2 ^{3}/$_4$"

This is a model of Guildford Castle in Surrey, although not an exact replica. The idea was suggested by the store that sold the first David Winter Cottage – *David Windsor's*, also of Guildford – and pieces made for them have a plaque sculpted on the side with the inscription Guildford Castle. This was removed for pieces being sold elsewhere, and the backstamp was changed from Guildford Castle to Castle Keep. Later pieces also have some of the windows filled in. Before sculpting it, David took pictures of the castle with his sister Alice standing in the foreground to give him an idea of the scale.

Considering pieces with the Guildford Castle inscription were only sold from one shop, they are very rare and consequently more valuable.

MARKINGS: © David Winter 1981

ISSUE PRICE:	£7	$N/A
CURRENT VALUE:	£750 – 1,000	$2,000 – 2,500
With inscription	£1,000+	$2,500+
UPDATE:	_____	

CHICHESTER CROSS

SCULPTED: 1981
LOCATION: 19 Ash Street
RETIRED: 1981
SIZE: Width: 3 ^{1}/$_2$" Depth: 3 ^{1}/$_2$" Height 4 ^{1}/$_4$"

This is the only David Winter Cottage not made from Crystacal. The detailed nature of the piece required an even stronger material, and resin was chosen. The suggestion for the piece came from the David Winter Cottage shop in Chichester, *Good Ideas*. It was very difficult to sculpt and to cast, and the purchase price was high (resin is more expensive than Crystacal). Consequently it had a short production life and only a small number were made, perhaps as few as a hundred. They hardly ever appear on the secondary market, and pieces with all the pinnacles above the buttresses intact are virtually non-existent.

Chichester Cross was not painted but dipped in three colour variations: stone white, stone grey and (later pieces) sandstone buff.

MARKINGS: None.

ISSUE PRICE:	£17	$N/A
CURRENT VALUE:	£1,300 – 1,500	$3,400 – 3,800
(If perfect	£2,500+	$6,000+)
UPDATE:	_____	

A CHRISTMAS CAROL

SCULPTED: 1989
LOCATION: Home Studio
RETIRED: Dec 1989
SIZE: Width: 6 ^{3}/$_8$" Depth: 4 ^{5}/$_8$" Height 5 ^{3}/$_4$"

The special piece for Christmas 1989, and the first to come in its own customised box. A Christmas Carol is highly regarded by collectors and for many it is a favourite.

MARKINGS: © David Winter 1989

ISSUE PRICE:	£46	$135
CURRENT VALUE:	£80 – 120	$140 – 180
UPDATE:	_____	

CHRISTMAS IN SCOTLAND AND HOGMANAY

(Usually abbreviated to 'HOGMANAY')
SCULPTED: 1988
LOCATION: Home Studio
RETIRED: Dec 1988
SIZE: Width: 6" Depth: 4 ^{3}/$_8$" Height 5 ^{1}/$_2$"

The special piece for Christmas 1988, and the only one of the 'Christmas Collection' not inspired by Charles Dickens' story *A Christmas Carol*. The icicles hanging from the roof are a novelty. They were made from a sort of clear resin and attached at the finishing stage.

MARKINGS: © David Winter 1988

ISSUE PRICE:	£46	$100
CURRENT VALUE:	£75 – 150	$150 – 200
UPDATE:	_____	

THE COACHING INN

SCULPTED: 1980
LOCATION: Manor Farm Craft Centre, Seale, near Farnham, Surrey.
RETIRED: 1983
SIZE: Width: 11 ^{1}/$_2$" Depth: 7 ^{1}/$_2$" Height 4 ^{1}/$_2$"

This was the most ambitious piece David had attemped at the time. He later took sections from it and developed them into new pieces – the thatched section at the back right became Rose Cottage and the main beamed front building developed into Tudor Manor House.

The door on the thatched building is recessed on very early models. Then this was cut away and some had a plain, slightly ribbed effect, until the final door was sculpted.

Early models have matchsticks as pillars of the balcony at the rear of the main front building. They were later cast in Crystacal and stuck on, and were much fatter.

The arched sign, 'The White Hart' over the front entrance to the courtyard was missing on later models. As the moulds aged, the two buildings on either side of the entrance began to bow outwards slightly, the gap between them increased, and the sign no longer fitted. A few were released with a section of matchstick at either side to fill the gap, but the result was unsatisfactory and it was decided to leave the sign off completely.

Coaching Inns are less common without the sign. Until quite recently replacement signs have been supplied from John Hine Studios, but collectors may have difficulty attaching them if the gap between the buildings is too wide.

MARKINGS: © David Winter 1980
ISSUE PRICE: £36 $165
CURRENT VALUE: £1,500 – 2,500 $4,500 – 6,000
UPDATE: _____

CORNISH COTTAGE
SCULPTED: 1982
LOCATION: Begun whilst on holiday in Cornwall and completed at 19 Ash Street.
RETIRED: 1986
SIZE: Width: 5 $^3/_8$" Depth: 2 $^3/_4$" Height 2 $^3/_4$"
This is generally claimed to be the only David Winter Cottage not to have David's signature on the base. This is incorrect. Several other pieces (Dove Cottage, Three Ducks Inn, The Forge, Little Forge) plus some pieces prior to restyling also lack a signature and date. David did actually put it on Cornish Cottage but he then reduced the size of the base, which at first was larger and had rocks around the cottage. In the process, the signature was removed, and David simply forgot to put it back on. No copies were ever released with the original signed base. Cornish Cottage was retired to make way for the West Country Collection.
MARKINGS: None
ISSUE PRICE: £8 $30
CURRENT VALUE: £400 – 600 $1,300 – 1,900
UPDATE: _____

CORNISH TIN MINE
SCULPTED: 1983
LOCATION: Home Studio
RETIRED: Jan 1989
SIZE: Width: 3 $^1/_4$" Depth: 2 $^1/_2$" Height: 5 $^1/_4$"
David Winter originally intended simply to modify this piece for relaunch with the 'West Country Collection' in 1987. But he got carried away, and the new piece was so different (especially with complex metal attachments) that it was renamed Cornish Engine House and classified as a brand new piece. (The same happened with Cotton Mill, which developed into Derbyshire Cotton Mill.) Whilst stocks of Cornish Tin Mine remained, the two pieces ran concurrently for a

while, until Cornish Tin Mine was officially retired in January 1989.

Early pieces have less foliage between the chimney stack and the mill building.

MARKINGS: © David Winter 1983
ISSUE PRICE: £7 $22
CURRENT VALUE: £50 – 75 $75 – 125
UPDATE: _____

COTSWOLD VILLAGE
SCULPTED: 1982
LOCATION: Hendon Road
RETIRED: 1990
SIZE: Width: 6 $^3/_4$" Depth: 4 $^1/_2$" Height 3 $^5/_8$"
Early pieces varied as modifications were made during the first year of production, mainly to make demoulding easier:
* The overhang of the church porch was shortened.
* Foliage was added to support the gravestones which stand to the left of the church door.
* Foliage was added to the church walls on all sides, and onto the roofs of several buildings (including the church).
* The gap between the church and the building to the right of the village street was blocked with greenery.
* As in The Village, arches of foliage linking buildings together were adopted to help the moulds keep their shape. There are two on Cotswold Village; one between the side of the church tower and the adjoining cottage, and another linking the front left buildings with the cottage behind and above it.
David Winter shaped Cotswold Village specifically so that it would be easy to photograph – low and open at the front, rising gradually towards the back. This impression is very strong when the piece is viewed from the front at 'ground level'.
MARKINGS: © David Winter 1982
ISSUE PRICE: £20 $60
CURRENT VALUE: £50 – 60 $85 – 110
UPDATE: _____

THE COTTON MILL
SCULPTED: 1983
LOCATION: Hendon Road
RETIRED: Jan 1989
SIZE: Width: 4 $^3/_8$" Depth: 3 $^3/_4$" Height 9 $^1/_8$"
Early models have no greenery growing between the chimney and the mill building. It was added to about three inches in height to strengthen the mould in 1984. David Winter intended to restyle Cotton Mill in late 1987, and the changes were

made; but the new version was held back to become part of the 'Midlands Collection' in Spring 1988 and renamed Derbyshire Cotton Mill. For classification purposes, the two are regarded as entirely separate pieces. Whilst existing stocks of Cotton Mill were sold, the two pieces ran concurrently until Cotton Mill was officially retired in January 1989.

Cotton Mill was very slow to take off on the secondary market, but curiously it is now very much in demand, as its selling price reflects.

MARKINGS: © David Winter 1983

ISSUE PRICE:	£14	$42
CURRENT VALUE:	£300 – 400	$800 – 1,000
UPDATE:	_____	

CROFTER'S COTTAGE
SCULPTED: 1986
LOCATION: 19 Ash Street
RETIRED: July 1989
SIZE: Width: 5" Depth: 3 ^{1}/2" Height 4 ^{3}/4"
Replaced by Scottish Crofters when the 'Scottish Collection' was launched, although identical apart from stone weights which were added to the thatched roof. Scottish Crofters became available in Spring 1989, so the two ran concurrently for several months until Crofter's Cottage retired at the end of July. Even then it remained available until exisiting stocks had been sold.

MARKINGS: © David Winter 1986

ISSUE PRICE:	£17	$51
CURRENT VALUE:	£40 – 70	$75 – 120
UPDATE:	_____	

DOUBLE OAST
SCULPTED: 1981
LOCATION: 19 Ash Street
RETIRED: 1982
SIZE: Width: 5 ^{1}/2" Depth: 4 ^{5}/8" Height 5 ^{3}/8"
Three Oasts were soon perceived to be unnecessary. People tended to choose either the Single or the Triple, so the Double was withdrawn. (Ironically it is now the most sought after, though very few ever reach the secondary market).

MARKINGS: David Winter

ISSUE PRICE:	£10	$N/A
CURRENT VALUE:	£1,500 – 1,800	$4,000 – 5,000
UPDATE:	_____	

DOVE COTTAGE
SCULPTED: 1980
LOCATION: The Coalshed
RETIRED: 1983
SIZE: Width: 6 ^{1}/4" Depth: 5 ^{5}/8" Height 3 ^{1}/2"

Not a model of Wordsworth's Lake District home of the same name, but an imaginary self-sufficient small-holding. Pieces may vary slightly due to distortions in the moulds. (This was common to all very early David Winter Cottages, a problem which technical improvements over the years have eradicated.)

There is no signature or date on the base.

Other variations in detail to watch out for:
* The woman sitting between the chimney breasts on the left side is sometimes headless, and on later pieces she has lost all definition and turned into a bush!
* More dovecotes are blocked on some models than others.
* Detail on the chimney varies depending on the amount of fettling.

MARKINGS: None

ISSUE PRICE:	£7.50	$60
CURRENT VALUE:	£650 – 900	$1,800 – 2,400
UPDATE:	_____	

EBENEZER SCROOGE'S COUNTING HOUSE
SCULPTED: 1987
LOCATION: Eggars Hill
RETIRED: Feb 1988
SIZE: Width: 5" Depth: 4 ^{5}/8" Height 6"
This was the first of a set of pieces that David has been sculpting in recent years, sometimes called the 'Christmas Collection'. A new piece is launched every year for the Christmas period. Availability is from September until New Year's Eve, and then all production moulds are destroyed. Ebenezer Scrooge's Counting House was the first – for Christmas 1987. The other pieces are:

Christmas in Scotland and Hogmanay (1988)
A Christmas Carol (1989)
Mr. Fezziwig's Emporium (1990)
Fred's Home – "Merry Christmas, uncle Ebenezer," said Scrooge's nephew Fred, "and a Happy New Year." (1991)

There are two versions of Ebenezer Scrooge's Counting House. At the back of the original piece, where the central and clock tower buildings join, there is a small bush. As production increased, the two buildings began to separate in the moulds; so, to strengthen the join, the bush was extended upwards in the corner to a height of about two and a half inches, creating the second version.

Unlike all the special Christmas pieces since, Ebenezer Scrooge's Counting House was not retired on New Year's Eve but on 29th February (1988 being a leap year), which was just as well, as the number of orders were far greater than anticipated by John Hine Studios and deliveries were being made well into 1988.

MARKINGS: © David Winter 1987

ISSUE PRICE:	£42	$97
CURRENT VALUE:	£175 – 250	$220 – 300
UPDATE:	_____	

FAIRYTALE CASTLE

SCULPTED: 1982
LOCATION: Hendon Road
RETIRED: July 1989
SIZE: Width: 6" Depth: 5 $^5/_8$" Height 10"

Very early pieces have sharply pointed tower caps, a foliage arch behind the main tower, and no foliage between the separate towers. But this proved very difficult to produce, and gradually changes were made:
* Tower caps were rounded off.
* More and more foliage was gradually added, binding the towers together.
* The original foliage arch was filled in, and two additional arches were added in 1984/5.

Mould shrinkage caused pieces made between 1983 and 1985 to become slightly smaller, but later models are the same size as early ones.

MARKINGS: © David Winter 1982

ISSUE PRICE:	£40	$115
CURRENT VALUE:	£125 – 200	$150 – 250
UPDATE:	_____	

FALSTAFF'S MANOR

SCULPTED: 1986
LOCATION: 19 Ash Street
RETIRED: 1990/91
SIZE: Width: 7" Depth: 6 $^1/_2$" Height 7 $^3/_4$"

A personal favourite of both David Winter and John Hine, and one of only a handful of pieces which David displays in his own home. Some confusion surrounds why a numbered limited edition of 10,000 was announced for North America whilst unnumbered pieces became available elsewhere. However all production ceased when number 10,000 was reached during 1990, although an official announcement was not made until early 1991.

Although Falstaff's Manor was launched in 1986, David was working on it in 1985.

MARKINGS: © David Winter 1986

ISSUE PRICE:	£115	$242
CURRENT VALUE:	£200 – 300	$350 – 550
UPDATE:	_____	

FRED'S HOME – "MERRY CHRISTMAS, UNCLE EBENEZER," SAID SCROOGE'S NEPHEW FRED, "AND A HAPPY NEW YEAR."

SCULPTED: 1990/91
LOCATION: Home Studio
RETIRED: Dec 91
SIZE: Width: 5" Depth: 4 $^5/_8$" Height 7 $^5/_8$"

The special Christmas piece for 1991. David Winter must have been working on this model well in advance as the blocked-up, undetailed wax original can be seen in the video *Meet The Artist*, which was filmed during the summer of 1990. The incredibly long name was chosen to define exactly who Fred is, i.e. Scrooge's nephew, and was not the first choice; Tiny Tim's House and Bob Cratchit's Dwelling were both possibilities. They were rejected because the sculpture was thought too grand for such impoverished characters. "Ebenezer" is mis-spelt on the customised box, with an extra 'e' (Ebeneezer).

MARKINGS: © David Winter 1990

ISSUE PRICE:	£60	$145
CURRENT VALUE:	£65 - 70	$150 - 160
UPDATE:	_____	

THE FORGE

SCULPTED: 1980
LOCATION: The Coalshed
RETIRED: 1983
SIZE: Width: 9" Depth: 5" Height 2 $^7/_8$"

Some models have more ivy than others growing between the main building and the outhouse. It has been thought for a long time that The Forge has no signature, name or date on the base. However, several examples have materialised recently to disclaim the theory. If there are others, they are probably rare.

On later pieces the inscription on the milestone set against the front wall wore away as the moulds deteriorated.

MARKINGS: None

ISSUE PRICE:	£9	$60
CURRENT VALUE:	£650 – 850	$2,300 – 3,000
UPDATE:	_____	

THE GRANGE

SCULPTED: 1988
LOCATION: Home Studio
RETIRED: 1989
SIZE: Width: 5 $^1/_4$" Depth: 4" Height 6 $^5/_8$"

The Grange created the biggest furore in the history of David Winter Cottages. The elaborate metal balcony proved to be a huge production problem for John Hine Studios, because Crystacal 'gives' slightly and metal doesn't;

consequently getting balconies to fit the pieces was a nightmare. In an attempt to discourage people from buying the piece, John Hine announced that the price was to double. Extraordinarily, this had the opposite effect, and orders increased. Faced with an impossible situation, John decided there was no alternative but to retire the piece immediately. As soon as the announcement was made in June 1989, prices mushroomed overnight, and suddenly The Grange was the most sought after David Winter Cottage on the secondary market, changing hands left, right and centre. T-shirts appeared declaring: I'd give the shirt off my back for a Grange. Prices have stabilised now, but during the height of 'Grange mania', they peaked at around $4,500.

John Hine then had the unenviable task of smashing all unsold copies of The Grange into a skip, with the help of Harry Hine and David Gravelle. Only one model escaped the cull; it was given to John's wife Rosie for bringing them a cup of tea. In the event it turned out to be a very generous tip!

MARKINGS: © David Winter 1988
ISSUE PRICE: £60 $120
CURRENT VALUE: £650 – 1,000 $1,200 – 2,000
UPDATE: _____

THE HAYBARN
SCULPTED: 1983
LOCATION: Hendon Road
RETIRED: 1987
SIZE: Width: 4 $^1/4$" Depth: 2 $^1/2$" Height 3"
The idea for this piece was sparked by an illustration of a real building in a book belonging to John Hine (as did Miner's Cottage). The original can be seen at the Welsh Folk Museum, St. Fagans, Cardiff, where it was re-erected after being moved from an estate in Wales.

MARKINGS: David Winter
ISSUE PRICE: £6 $22
CURRENT VALUE: £100 – 150 $400 – 600
UPDATE: _____

HERMITS HUMBLE HOME
SCULPTED: 1985
LOCATION: Hendon Road
RETIRED: 1988
SIZE: Width: 4 $^1/2$" Depth: 3 $^3/4$" Height 5 $^1/2$"
Modifications to the trees were made during the first year of production. Later models have gaps filled up with foliage to simplify casting and demoulding.

The four pieces retired together on June 1st 1988

(Hermits Humble Home, House of the Master Mason, House on Top and Woodcutters Cottage) are sometimes referred to as David's 'Fantasy Series'. The title appears to have materialised from collectors and has never been used officially by John Hine Studios.

All four pieces are very popular on the secondary market.

MARKINGS: © David Winter 1985
ISSUE PRICE: £32 $87
CURRENT VALUE: £200 – 250 $200 – 300
UPDATE: _____

HOUSE OF THE MASTER MASON
SCULPTED: 1984
LOCATION: Hendon Road
RETIRED: 1988
SIZE: Width: 5" Depth: 3 $^3/4$" Height 6 $^1/2$"
One of only two David Winter Cottages to date (the other is The Cooper's Cottage) to have pantiles rather than ordinary roof tiles – a sophisticated feature one might expect from a master mason.

MARKINGS: © David Winter 1984
ISSUE PRICE: £32 $75
CURRENT VALUE: £150 – 200 $250 – 300
UPDATE: _____

HOUSE ON TOP
SCULPTED: 1982
LOCATION: Hendon Road
RETIRED: 1988
SIZE: 4 $^7/8$" Depth: 4 $^1/2$" Height 6 $^1/8$"
A small number of early pieces have a sheer drop from outside the main door of the top house into the cave below. These are very rare.

From 1984 onwards the piece was standard, but in the first two years of production, foliage was gradually added to block up gaps behind the supports under the overhanging buildings. Eventually they were all filled.

This main door is half open and behind it an alley way runs right through the building. In the middle of the alley are two staggered half-doors; on some later pieces one of them is missing. Towards the end of production, as moulds deteriorated, the door disappeared completely on a few pieces.

MARKINGS: © David Winter 1982
ISSUE PRICE: £32 $92
CURRENT VALUE: £200 – 250 $250 – 350
UPDATE: _____

LITTLE FORGE

SCULPTED: 1980
LOCATION: The Coalshed
RETIRED: 1983
SIZE: Width: 5 $^1/_2$" Depth: 3 $^3/_4$" Height 2 $^1/_2$"
Just as Little Mill (original) derives from the original Mill House, Little Forge is the main building of The Forge, minus the stable to the left, the tree to the right, and all the surrounding base. The piece was neither signed nor dated by David Winter.
Compared to The Forge, Little Forge is very rare. Few ever find their way onto the secondary market.
MARKINGS: None

ISSUE PRICE:	£4.50	$40
CURRENT VALUE:	£700 – 1,000	$2,100 – 2,900
UPDATE:	_____	

LITTLE MILL (original)

SCULPTED: 1980
LOCATION: The Coalshed
RETIRED: 1980
SIZE: Width: 5 $^1/_4$" Depth: 4 $^1/_2$" Height 2 $^3/_4$"
This was taken from the central building of the original Mill House (a squat T-shape) with the mill wheel and all surrounding base removed. There was no name or date on the base.
MARKINGS: None

ISSUE PRICE:	£4.50	$N/A
CURRENT VALUE:	£1,500 – 1,750	$2,300 – 3,200
UPDATE:	_____	

MARK 2

SCULPTED: 1980
LOCATION: The Coalshed
RETIRED: 1983
SIZE: Width: 5 $^5/_8$" Depth: 3 $^1/_8$" Height 3"
Just as the original Little Mill derived from the original Mill House, so Little Mill Mark 2 derived from the restyled Mill House, each intended as a companion piece for the other. The stem of the T-shaped mill was removed to create a simple rectangular building, and a water wheel was added to the left side. A plaque reading "The Little Mill. David Winter 1980" was sculpted to the rear of the base but is not strictly a base marking.
MARKINGS: See above

ISSUE PRICE:	£4.50	$40
CURRENT VALUE:	£1,000 – 1,300	$1,900 – 2,500
UPDATE:	_____	

MARK 3

SCULPTED: 1980
LOCATION: The Coalshed
RETIRED: 1983
SIZE: Width: 5 $^5/_8$" Depth: 3 $^1/_8$" Height 3"
Very similar to Mark 2. The space between the building and the mill wheel caused problems with the moulds, so greenery was added to fill the gap, which is the distinctive characteristic of Mark 3. The plaque was also removed, and this version, like Mark 1, does not have David's name on it.
MARKINGS: None

ISSUE PRICE:	£4.50	$40
CURRENT VALUE:	£900 – 1,100	$1,700 – 2,300
UPDATE:	_____	

MILL HOUSE (original)

SCULPTED: 1980
LOCATION: The Coalshed
RETIRED: 1980
SIZE: Width: 9 $^1/_4$" Depth: 6 $^1/_2$" Height 3 $^1/_2$"
The very first Cottage sculpted by David Winter and a very rare piece indeed in its original form. A plaque on its side reads 'THE MILL HOUSE, ENGLAND, © DAVID WINTER'. It was remodelled in the same year that it was made, and so very few were produced in the original format with the wide base, river and outbuilding to the rear left. The beam work is almost flush with the building walls and the detail characteristic of David's later work has yet to emerge.
MARKINGS: None.

ISSUE PRICE:	£7.50	$N/A
CURRENT PRICE:	£1,500 – 2,000	$2,500 – 3,000
UPDATE:	_____	

MILL HOUSE (remodelled)

SCULPTED: 1980
LOCATION: The Coalshed
RETIRED: 1983
SIZE: Width: 8" Depth: 4 $^5/_8$" Height 3 $^1/_4$"
The revised Mill House is different from the original, although the basic mill building is the same. It is a smaller piece, with the base pared down considerably. Beam work is much more prominent and the water wheel has been sculpted in more detail. The overall impression is of a more finely detailed piece. Far more of this version were made than of the original, with a production run lasting several years instead of a few months.
MARKINGS: None

ISSUE PRICE:	£7.50	$50
CURRENT PRICE:	£1,000 – 1,250	$1,900 – 2,600
UPDATE:	_____	

MINER'S COTTAGE
SCULPTED: 1982
LOCATION: Hendon Road
RETIRED: 1987
SIZE: Width: 3 $^3/_8$" Depth: 1 $^3/_8$" Height 2 $^3/_8$"
Miner's Cottage is based on an illustration from the same book that inspired The Haybarn.
MARKINGS: David Winter

ISSUE PRICE:	£6	$22
CURRENT VALUE:	£100 – 150	$300 – 450
UPDATE:	_____	

MR FEZZIWIG'S EMPORIUM
SCULPTED: 1990
LOCATION: Faith Winter's studio
RETIRED: Dec 1990
SIZE: Width: 5" Depth: 4 $^1/_2$" Height 6"
The special Christmas piece for 1990. Mr. Fezziwig is a character from Dickens' *A Christmas Carol*, although the word 'emporium' is never used in the story to describe his premises. Nevertheless it is an appealing name. David Winter can be seen at work actually sculpting this piece in the video, *Meet The Artist*, produced by John Hine Studios.
MARKINGS: © David Winter 1989

ISSUE PRICE:	£60	$135
CURRENT VALUE:	£75 – 90	$135 – 180
UPDATE:	_____	

MOORLAND COTTAGE
SCULPTED: 1982
LOCATION: Hendon Road
RETIRED: 1987
SIZE: Width: 2 $^3/_4$" Depth: 2 $^3/_4$" Height 2 $^1/_4$"
MARKINGS: David Winter

ISSUE PRICE:	£6	$22
CURRENT VALUE:	£100 – 150	$250 – 350
UPDATE:	_____	

THE OLD CURIOSITY SHOP
SCULPTED: 1980
RELEASED: 1981
LOCATION: Parents' home
RETIRED: 1983
SIZE: Width: 4 $^3/_4$" Depth: 2 $^7/_8$" Height 3 $^3/_4$"
This piece was sculpted in mid-winter on David's parents' dining room table (because it was too cold to work in the coalshed) and is a model of the shop in Portsmouth Street, Lincoln's Inn, London, immortalised by Charles Dickens in his novel of the same name. Whilst in production, the piece could actually be purchased at the real Old Curiosity Shop.
David Winter has identified five versions of the piece, determined by the numerous methods devised to create a shop window glass effect in front of a beautifully detailed window display. In chronological order, they are as follows:
(1) – The window front frame was cast separately and glued into place; then clear imbedding resin was poured in through the windows.
(2) – The window frame and a sheet of clear imbedding resin were glued on, one on top of the other.
(3) – Same as (2), but using a sheet of clear acetate cut to size instead of imbedding resin.
(4) – Same as (2), but using clear reflector plastic (as used on bicycle reflectors) instead of imbedding resin.
(5) – The window display was completely blanked out and the frame cast as part of the piece.
Somewhere in the window display is a tiny model of the Old Curiosity Shop itself!
The most extraordinary aspect of the piece is the back, which is cut away to reveal the inside of the shop in a mass of detail. A scene taken from an illustration by Phiz is portrayed. This unusual approach was taken because the real building now backs onto a modern office block and was not available to be sculpted. The scene includes a man who can be seen peering through a curtain. He is missing on very early pieces.
MARKINGS: © David Winter 1980

ISSUE PRICE:	£10	$40
CURRENT VALUE:	£600 – 800	$1,800 – 2,400
UPDATE:	_____	

ORCHARD COTTAGE
SCULPTED: 1986
LOCATION: North Studio, Eggars Hill.
RETIRED: Nov 1991
SIZE: Width: 7 $^1/_8$" Depth: 4 $^3/_4$" Height: 4 $^3/_4$"
For some reason this piece was sculpted in the North Studio at Eggars Hill when the mouldmaking department was based there. David can't remember why! Orchard Cottage surprised just about all collectors when it was retired, as Lacemakers or Single Oast had been tipped to disappear with Bottle Kiln.
MARKINGS: © David Winter 1987

ISSUE PRICE:	£42	$91
CURRENT VALUE:	£60 – 80	$125 – 150
UPDATE:	_____	

PROVENCAL ONE
SCULPTED: 1980
RELEASED: 1981
LOCATION: The Coalshed
RETIRED: 1981
SIZE: Width: 5" Depth: 3 $^3/_4$" Height 3"

The Provencal pieces (Provencal One, Provencal Two, Provencal Tiny A and B) were made for and sold almost exclusively in the South of France during 1981 with John Hine's son Harry (aged 13 at the time) being given the job of selling them. A few were sold, some were destroyed, and they are unheard of on the secondary market.

Nevertheless, some models were sold in the U.K., and John Hine Studios were supplying shops with very small quantities in 1982.

Because of the 'notoriety' of Provencal Two, created by its absence even from the collection at Eggars Hill, Provencal One's potential value on the secondary market has been somewhat ignored. The same number of both pieces were made, and they are therefore equally as rare.

Although released in 1981, Provencal One and Two must have been sculpted the year before because they both appear in the first David Winter Cottages booklet, which predates even The Coaching Inn (mentioned as David's 'latest work' but not illustrated.).

MARKINGS: None

ISSUE PRICE:	£7.50	$N/A
CURRENT VALUE:	£5,000+	$15,000+
UPDATE:	_____	

PROVENCAL TWO

SCULPTED: 1980
RELEASED: 1981
LOCATION: The Coalshed
RETIRED: 1981
SIZE: (APPROX.) Width: 7" Depth: 3 $^1/_2$" Height 3"

This is the only retired David Winter Cottage that John Hine Studios do not possess in the collection at Eggars Hill; nor do David Winter or John Hine own one personally. This instigated John Hine to launch a 'Quest for Provencal Two' in Cottage Country (No.11 - Autumn '89), and a lady responded and was featured in a subsequent issue. Collectors were invited to bid for the piece via John Hine Studios, and the lady's identity remained a secret (she was referred to only as Mrs X). The outcome of the bidding is unknown.

Faked copies of Provencal Two did appear briefly on the market during 1991, but the source was identified and closed down quite rapidly. Nevertheless, if the pieces do appear on the secondary market they should be examined for obvious signs of forgery (see Chapter Three).

MARKINGS: None

ISSUE PRICE:	£7.50	$N/A
CURRENT VALUE:	£8,000+	$15,000+
UPDATE:	_____	

QUAYSIDE

SCULPTED: 1980
LOCATION: The Coalshed
RETIRED: 1985
SIZE: Width: 6 $^3/_8$" Depth: 3 $^3/_4$" Height 4 $^1/_2$"

Despite its long production run, Quayside is now a much sought after piece and commands a surprisingly high price on the secondary market.

MARKINGS: © David Winter 1980

ISSUE PRICE:	£9	$60
CURRENT VALUE:	£750 – 950	$1,700 – 2,300
UPDATE:	_____	

SABRINA'S COTTAGE

SCULPTED: 1982
LOCATION: Hendon Road
RETIRED: 1982
SIZE: Width: 2" Depth: 2" Height 2 $^3/_4$"

A rare piece. John Hine believes that probably no more than 100 were ever released. It didn't sell well because it was such an unusual David Winter Cottage, and as John Hine Studios were in two minds whether or not to market it at all, it was soon withdrawn. The piece was sculpted by David as a gift to celebrate the birth of Sabrina, the daughter of David Gravelle, one of John Hine Studio's earliest members, and has the inscription: FOR SABRINA GRAVELLE 25/3/82 David Winter.

MARKINGS: See above

ISSUE PRICE:	£5.50	$N/A
CURRENT VALUE:	£1,000 – 1,300	$2,500 – 3,000
UPDATE:	_____	

ST.PAUL'S CATHEDRAL

SCULPTED: 1981
LOCATION: 19 Ash Street
RETIRED: 1982
SIZE: Width: 5 $^5/_8$" Depth: 3 $^1/_4$" Height 3 $^1/_2$"

Sculpted to celebrate the Royal Wedding between Prince Charles and Lady Diana Spencer, which took place inside St. Paul's Cathedral in 1981. The piece was sold with a commemorative wrap-around sleeve on the box. Later models suffered from loss of detail and distortion as the moulds bowed.

MARKINGS: None

ISSUE PRICE	£9	$N/A
CURRENT VALUE:	£700 – 900	$2,500 – 2,800
UPDATE:	_____	

SPINNER'S COTTAGE

SCULPTED: 1984
LOCATION: Home Studio
RETIRED: Apr 1991
SIZE: Width: 2 $^1/_2$" Depth: 2 $^1/_8$" Height 4"

Spinners Cottage was thought to be a surprising choice to withdraw from the Collection in 1991, but it is in fact a difficult piece to produce. Demoulding is particularly tricky because the top of the piece is as wide (if not slightly wider) than the base, and the whole piece has to be pulled through the mould opening at the base.

MARKINGS: © David Winter 1984

ISSUE PRICE:	£9	$27
CURRENT VALUE:	£25 – 40	$50 – 80
UPDATE:		

SQUIRES HALL

SCULPTED: 1985
LOCATION: Home Studio
RETIRED: 1990
SIZE: Width: 5 $^1/_2$" Depth: 4" Height 6 $^3/_4$"
MARKINGS: © David Winter 1985

ISSUE PRICE:	£37	$92
CURRENT VALUE:	£70 – 80	$130 – 150
UPDATE:		

SUFFOLK HOUSE

SCULPTED: 1985
LOCATION: Hendon Road
RETIRED: Jul 1989
SIZE: Width: 3 $^5/_8$" Depth: 3" Height 4 $^1/_4$"
On early pieces the main body of Suffolk House was painted white, whilst later ones were pink. Fewer white pieces were made than pink.

MARKINGS: © David Winter 1985

ISSUE PRICE:	£22	$49
CURRENT VALUE:	£50 – 100	$80 – 130
UPDATE:		

THREE DUCKS INN

SCULPTED: 1980
LOCATION: The Coalshed
RETIRED: 1983
SIZE: Width: 7 $^3/_8$" Depth: 5 $^3/_8$" Height 3 $^1/_4$"
There is no signature or date on the base on this, the third piece David Winter made. The name The Three Ducks appears engraved on the pub wall, and the two public doors have SNUG and SALOON BAR embossed upon them. David says that nowadays incorporating such details would be easy, but in 1980 this was quite a technical challenge when it came to mouldmaking. In fact the words SNUG and SALOON BAR wore off the mould eventually, and on some pieces they are missing. A delightful feature of this piece is the post box sunk into the pub wall – on the front right side.

Although £7.50 was the original selling price, some must have been sold for even less – David has one in his house with the original price tag of £4.95 on the base!

MARKINGS: None

ISSUE PRICE:	£7.50	$N/A
CURRENT VALUE:	£800 – 1,000	$2,600 – 2,900
UPDATE:		

TUDOR MANOR HOUSE

SCULPTED: 1985
LOCATION: Parents' dining room
RETIRED: Jul 1991
SIZE: Width: 4 $^3/_4$" Depth: 3 $^1/_2$" Height 4 $^1/_2$"
The original was sculpted on David's parents' dining room table, but the remodelling took place at 19 Ash Street.

On very early pieces the balcony had a recess to left and right of it forming a long walkway, but very few were made like this before the recesses were blocked up due to moulding and casting difficulties. A larger number of early pieces were made in which the balcony was cast separately and glued into place. It was later cast as part of the main piece.

Meanwhile the piece lost detail and was virtually remade by David Winter in 1985, although before this the name plate with Tudor Manor House written on it disappeared off some models.

Excluding the filled-in recesses, here are the main differences between a 1981 and a 1985 piece:

ORIGINAL	REMODELLED
Balcony cast separately and glued into place.	Balcony cast as part of main model.
Two sets of stairs between chimney breasts on right side.	Only one set of stairs between chimney breasts.
Large bay window at front.	No bay window.
Chimney short and blunt.	Chimney $^1/_2$" taller (rising above roof level) and squared off.
Tudor Manor House name plate on edge of base.	Name plate removed.
No foliage.	Foliage in various places.

Other alterations in 1985 include:
* All windows enlarged.

* Three gables on inner roof enlarged.
* Two brick walls extended around the front of the base.
* Small cellar window added to front right.
* Beamwork enlarged, and some beams removed.
* Two front staircases widened.
* Doorway under balcony on right reduced in size.

David worked on these alterations at the same time as he was sculpting Falstaff's Manor.

MARKINGS: © David Winter 1981

ISSUE PRICE:	£6	$47
CURRENT VALUE:	£50 – 75	$100 – 200
UPDATE:		

TYTHE BARN

SCULPTED: 1981
LOCATION: 19 Ash Street
RETIRED: 1986
SIZE: Width: 6 $1/4$" Depth: 4" Height 3 $1/2$"

Original title – Farm Barn. This model is based on a rather dilapidated old barn near Bordon which David drove past one day. It still stands today and can be found in Hampshire on the B3004 between the village of Kingsley and the junction with the Farnham to Bordon road (A325). Early models have painted matchsticks as posts, holding up the covered area. These were later changed to Crystacal, cast separately and glued into place. On the right of the piece there are two horses poking their heads out of stable doors. On some models one or both heads are missing, as it was very difficult to avoid air pockets in the mould. (David actually used toy dogs on his wax sculpture; scaled down, they look just like horses.)

Between 1981 and 1983, Tythe Barn was made with the right hand door standing ajar. It was very flimsy, easily broken and difficult to cast. So a second version was produced, with the open barn door off its hinges and sculpted lying on the floor. The first version (with the door standing) is less common than the second – and more valuable.

(A middle version also exists, with the door cast separately and glued on.)

MARKINGS: David Winter

ISSUE PRICE:	£11	$39
CURRENT VALUES:		
(Door On)	£900 – 1,100	$2,000 – 2,600
(Door Off)	£700 – 850	$1,600 – 2,000
UPDATE:		

WILLIAM SHAKESPEARE'S BIRTHPLACE

(Large)
SCULPTED: 1982
LOCATION: 19 Ash Street
RETIRED: 1984
SIZE: Width: 6 $3/8$" Depth: 4 $7/8$" Height 3 $1/4$"

A second, large version of the Bard's birthplace was sculpted because the David Winter Cottage stockist in Stratford-Upon-Avon happened to be located right opposite the real thing. David Winter received help from Tim Moore, John Hine Studio's Chief Mouldmaker for many years, in working on this piece. Tim blocked it up and put all the tiles on, with David adding all the fine detail.

(A medium-sized version of William Shakespeare's Birthplace was also released by John Hine Studios, but it was sculpted by Malcolm Cooper and not by David Winter.)

MARKINGS: © David Winter 1980

ISSUE PRICE:	£23	$60
CURRENT VALUE:	£500 – 800	$1,800 – 2,300
UPDATE:		

WOODCUTTER'S COTTAGE

SCULPTED: 1983
LOCATION: Home Studio
RETIRED: 1988
SIZE: Width: 4 $1/2$" Depth: 4 $1/4$" Height 5 $7/8$"

Pieces made between 1983 and 1985 have a more pointed tip to the tall, central tree stump. It was smoothed down to ease demoulding. This piece was known as Bert, then Tree House before finally receiving the official name Woodcutter's Cottage.

MARKINGS: © David Winter 1984

ISSUE PRICE:	£33	$87
CURRENT VALUE:	£200 – 250	$250 – 350
UPDATE:		

TINY SERIES

SCULPTED: 1980
(Except Provencal A & B – 1981)
LOCATION: The Coalshed
RETIRED: 1982
Provencal A & B were later additions to the Tiny Series and were sculpted at the same time as the two larger Provencal pieces. All six of the original Tiny Series are models of existing buildings.

WILLIAM SHAKESPEARE'S BIRTHPLACE
SIZE: Width: 2 $^5/_8$" Depth: 1 $^5/_8$" Height: 1 $^1/_4$"
The great playright's birthplace can be seen to this day in the centre of Stratford-Upon-Avon, Warwickshire.
MARKINGS: © D.W.
ISSUE PRICE: £2 $N/A
CURRENT VALUE: £300 – 500 $1,000 – 1,500
UPDATE: _____

ANNE HATHAWAY'S COTTAGE
SIZE: Width: 3 $^3/_8$" Depth: 1 $^3/_4$" Height: 1 $^3/_8$"
This beautiful cottage at Shottery, Stratford-Upon-Avon, was the home of ten generations of Hathaways. Shakespeare married Anne Hathaway when he was eighteen and she was twenty-six. A few of the very early models had taller chimneys than the standard piece before they were shortened to simplify demoulding.
MARKINGS: © D.W.
ISSUE PRICE: £2 $N/A
CURRENT VALUE: £300 – 500 $1,000 – 1,500
UPDATE: _____

SULGRAVE MANOR
SIZE: Width: 3 $^1/_4$" Depth: 2" Height: 1 $^3/_8$"
The ancestral home of George Washington in Northamptonshire. The family coat of arms is sculpted onto the front of the model. The crest was difficult to paint and so a handful of pieces were produced in terracotta to be sold unpainted. They were test marketed at David Windsor's shop in Guilford but did not prove popular.
MARKINGS: © D.W.
ISSUE PRICE: £2 $N/A
CURRENT VALUE: £300 – 500 $1,000 – 1,500
UPDATE: _____

COTSWOLD FARMHOUSE
SIZE: Width: 1 $^5/_8$" Depth: 1 $^3/_4$" Height: 1 $^3/_8$"
The first of the Tiny Series to be sculpted. This is an existing building, but its precise whereabouts has not yet been uncovered.

MARKINGS: © D.W.
ISSUE PRICE: £2 $N/A
CURRENT VALUE: £300 – 500 $1,000 – 1,500
UPDATE: _____

CROWN INN
SIZE: Width: 2 $^7/_8$" Depth: 1 $^3/_4$" Height: 1 $^3/_8$"
The village pub at Chiddingfold, Surrey. At the front of the piece is the inscription: CROWN INN CHIDDINGFOLD AD 1285.
MARKINGS: © D.W.
ISSUE PRICE: £2 $N/A
CURRENT VALUE: £300 – 500 $1,000 – 1,500
UPDATE: _____

ST NICHOLAS' CHURCH
SIZE: Width: 3" Depth: 1 $^3/_4$" Height: 1 $^3/_4$"
This is a model of St. Nicholas' Church, Compton, Surrey – though not an exact copy. The steeple on the real building is covered in wooden shingles, but painters tended to interpret them on the model as tiles. The spire point varies slightly from one piece to another, due to casting difficulties. At one time, some white, unpainted pieces were sold in Compton village shop as wedding cake decorations for people who were getting married in the church.
MARKINGS: © D.W.
ISSUE PRICE: £2 $N/A
CURRENT VALUE: £300 – 500 $1,300 – 1,800
UPDATE: _____

PROVENCAL A
SIZE: Width: 2 $^3/_4$" Depth: 1 $^1/_2$" Height: 1 $^1/_4$"
Not as rare as the larger Provencals One and Two, because as part of the Tiny Series, Provencal A and B were in production longer.
MARKINGS: © D.W. A
ISSUE PRICE: £3 $N/A
CURRENT VALUE: £750 – 950 $1,600 – 2,400
UPDATE: _____

PROVENCAL B
SIZE: Width: 2 $^7/_8$" Depth: 1 $^1/_4$" Height: 1 $^5/_8$"
John Hine Studios are usually very resourceful when it comes to giving pieces interesting and evocative names. However Provencals One, Two, A and B must class as their least imaginitive offerings to date.
MARKINGS: © D.W. B
ISSUE PRICE: £3 $N/A
CURRENT VALUE: £750 – 950 $1,600 – 2,400
UPDATE: _____

The Original Mill House

Mill House remodelled

Dove Cottage

Three Ducks Inn

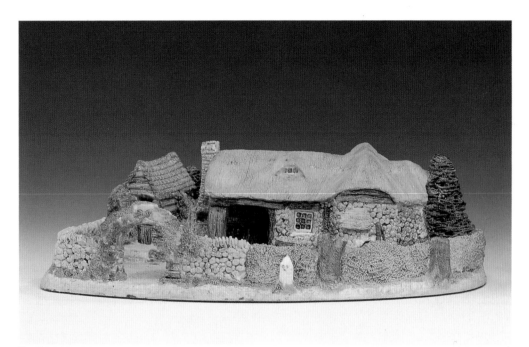

The Forge

Little Forge

Little Mill (original)

The Coaching Inn

Little Mill Mark 2 and Little Mill Mark 3

(L to R) St Nicholas' Church, Cotswold Farmhouse, Crown Inn. (St Nicholas' Church courtesy of Chris Billins)

(L. to R.) Anne Hathaway's Cottage, William Shakespeare's Birthplace, Sulgrave Manor

Provencal Two (Photograph courtesy of John Hine Studios)

Provencal Two. Rear view (Photograph courtesy of John Hine Studios)

Provencal One with Provencal Tiny B. (left) and Provencal Tiny A

Quayside

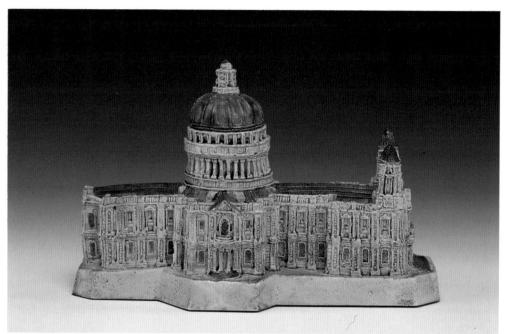

St. Paul's Cathedral

Chichester Cross in conventional resin and cold cast bronze – one of only six made. (Bronze courtesy of Chris Billins)

Tythe Barn. Original with door in place

Tythe Barn remodelled with door lying on the ground

Castle Keep (without the Guildford Castle plaque). Double Oast

The Old Curiosity Shop. An early (left) and late version

Blacksmith's Cottage. Miner's Cottage

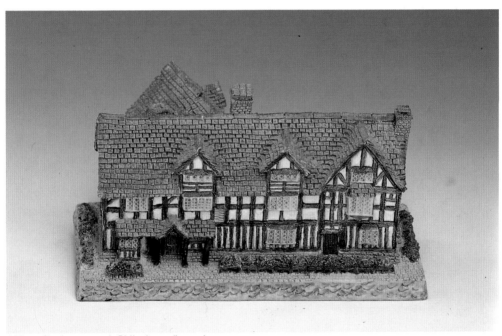

William Shakespeare's Birthplace (Large)

Sabrina's Cottage

Moorland Cottage

Cornish Cottage

60

Fairytale Castle

Cotswold Village

Spinners Cottage (left) and Brookside Hamlet

House on Top (Courtesy of Chris Billins)

The Haybarn

The Alms Houses

Hermit's Humble Home. Woodcutter's Cottage

Squires Hall. House of the Master Mason

Falstaff's Manor

Suffolk House in its two colour variations - pink (early) and white

Cornish Tin Mine (left) and its remodelled counterpart Cornish Engine House

Cotton Mill and its remodelled counterpart Derbyshire Cotton Mill. (Original Cotton Mill courtesy of Chrie Billins)

Crofter's Cottage (left) and its remodelled counterpart Scottish Crofters

Bottle Kiln (left) and Orchard Cottage

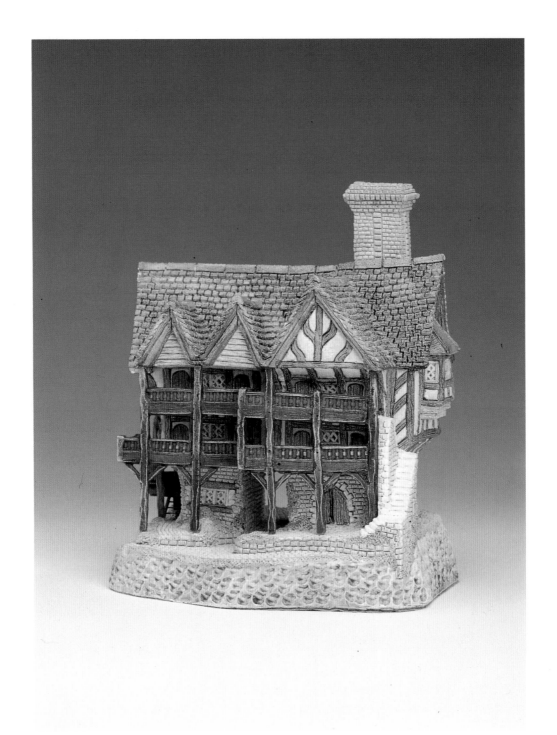

The Grange

Ebenezer Scrooge's Counting House

Christmas in Scotland and Hogmanay. Fred's Home – "Merry Christmas, Uncle Ebeneezer, " said Scrooge's nephew Fred, "and a Happy New Year."

Mister Fezziwig's Emporium. A Christmas Carol

Village Scene (left), the free gift for 1987 and '88 Guild members. Robin Hood's Hideaway (right), the first 1987 special Guild piece

Queen Elizabeth Slept Here, the second 1987 special Guild piece

The Bas-Relief Plaque (also called Street Scene), the free gift for 1989 Guild members

Black Bess Inn (left) and The Pavilion, the 1988 Guild special pieces

The Coal Shed (left) and Home Guard, the 1989 Guild special pieces

The Plucked Ducks, the free gift for 1990 Guild members

The Cobbler (left) and The Pottery, the 1990 Guild special pieces

Pershore Mill, the free gift for 1991 Guild members

Tomfool's Cottage (left) and Will-o'-the-Wisp, the 1991 Guild special pieces

Irish Water Mill

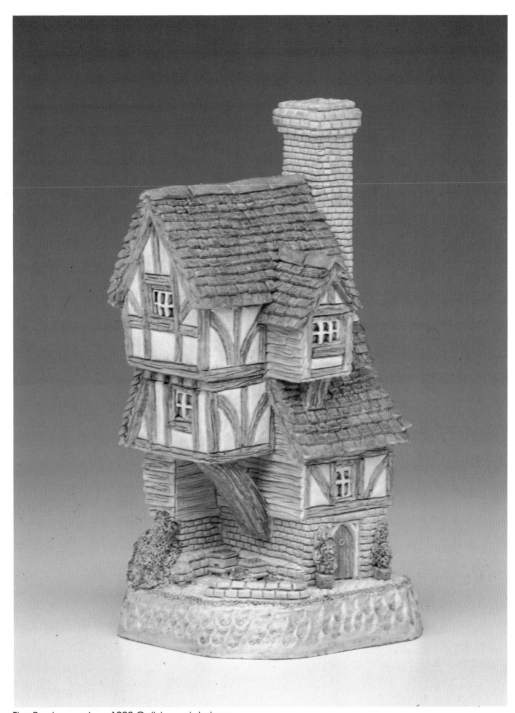

The Beekeeper's, a 1992 Guild special piece

The Candlemaker's, a 1992 Guild special piece

7 - THE GUILD

THE DAVID WINTER COTTAGES COLLECTORS GUILD

The Guild was established in 1987 to provide information and additional pieces to collectors of David Winter Cottages. It has proven extremely popular, with membership numbers growing worldwide. The Guild Magazine, *Cottage Country*, curently has a print-run of 40,000, and no wonder: it is remarkable value for money.

Membership fees for 1992 remain the same as they were in 1987 – UK £25, US $40, and equivalent prices in other currencies – which entitle you to a free David Winter piece, plus the option to purchase two additional David Winter Cottages, all of them available exclusively to Guild members and consequently limited edition pieces. (The redemption rate of Guild pieces averages around 50%). The quarterly Guild magazine, provides background information about David's work, details of new and forthcoming pieces, and letters from collectors worldwide.

The free Guild membership piece has until 1992 always been flat-backed: Village Scene, Street Scene, The Plucked Ducks and Pershore Mill, the last two being supplied in a shadow box. This tradition has been broken with Irish Water Mill, which is a free-standing piece.

Another recent change has affected availability of the two optional Guild pieces which are offered annually. Up to and including 1991 each piece was available for up to two years in the U.K. and three years in North America (to cater for the extended delivery time). But the 1992 pieces, The Beekeeper's and The Candlemaker's, will only be available until 31st December 1992 worldwide. The new system will very likely continue in future years.

Listed here are all the special Guild pieces sculpted by David Winter. Pieces are classified as 'retired' if their period of redemption is now over.

SPECIAL GUILD PIECES

VILLAGE SCENE
SCULPTED: 1986
LOCATION: Home Studio
RETIRED: 1988
SIZE: Width: 4 3/4" Depth: 1 3/8" Height: 7 3/8"
REMARKS: The free Guild Membership piece for 1987 and 1988. The piece is a slight variation on a point of sale which many DWC stockists displayed (and still do sometimes) with DAVID WINTER COTTAGES on the oval plaque.
MARKINGS: None

ISSUE PRICE:	£NIL	$NIL
CURRENT VALUE	E:100 – 150	$250 – 450
UPDATE:		

ROBIN HOOD'S HIDEAWAY
SCULPTED: 1986
LOCATION: Home Studio
RETIRED: 1989
SIZE: Width: 4 3/4" Depth: 4" Height: 4 3/8"
REMARKS: The first special Guild piece which members had the option to purchase. There are colour variations on the flowers; early pieces have red flowers, later ones have blue and yellow. Audrey White explains that she was on holiday when this piece was originated with red flowers. When she returned to work, she pointed out that Robin Hood's Hideaway would be situated deep in the heart of a forest, where red flowers would not grow. So blues and yellows were adopted instead, suggesting bluebells and primroses.
Early pieces also have a bolder colour on the tree trunk, which was later changed to a silvery grey.
MARKINGS: Guild No. 1 © David Winter Sept. 1986

ISSUE PRICE:	£18	$54
CURRENT VALUE:	£250 – 350	$350 – 550
UPDATE:		

QUEEN ELIZABETH SLEPT HERE

SCULPTED: 1987
LOCATION: Home Studio
RETIRED: 1989
SIZE: Width: 8" Depth: $5^3/4$" Height: $6^1/2$"
A magnificent sculpture which was regarded as expensive at the time. Ironically it was underpriced by John Hine Studios and became something of a liability! Queen Elizabeth Slept Here and Robin Hood's Hideaway are the only two pieces to be marked on the base with the month in which David completed sculpting them as well as the year.
MARKINGS: Guild No.2 © David Winter May 1987
ISSUE PRICE: £70 $183
CURRENT VALUE: £200 – 300 $400 – 550
UPDATE: _____

BLACK BESS INN

SCULPTED: 1988
LOCATION: Home Studio
RETIRED: 1990
SIZE: Width: $5^5/8$" Depth: $4^3/8$" Height: 5"
The name derives from highwayman Dick Turpin's legendary horse, Black Bess.
MARKINGS: Guild No. 3 © David Winter 1988
ISSUE PRICE: £25 $60
CURRENT VALUE: £150 – 250 $180 – 300
UPDATE: _____

THE PAVILION

SCULPTED: 1988
LOCATION: Home Studio
RETIRED: 1990
SIZE: Width: $5^3/8$" Depth: $3^3/4$" Height: $4^1/2$"
The incorrect spelling 'PAVILLION' was used on the backstamp, box and most literature, and has only been corrected in retrospect.
MARKINGS: Guild No. 4 © David Winter 1988
ISSUE PRICE: £23 $52
CURRENT VALUE: £150 – 220 $200 – 300
UPDATE: _____

STREET SCENE (The Bas-Relief Plaque)

SCULPTED: 1989
LOCATION: Home Studio
RETIRED: Dec 1989
SIZE: (Circular) Diameter: $8^1/4$"
The free Guild Membership piece for 1989. Launched originally as the Bas-Relief Plaque, the name Street Scene was adopted later. This piece was something of a technical challenge for David Winter, and he spent a long time getting the perspective right. No one can deny that as a free piece Street Scene has been the most generous Guild offering to date.
MARKINGS: © David Winter 1989
ISSUE PRICE: £NIL $ NIL
CURRENT VALUE: £100 – 150 $150 – 250
UPDATE: _____

HOME GUARD

SCULPTED: 1988
LOCATION: Home Studio
RELEASED: 1989
RETIRED: 1991
SIZE: Width: $5^3/4$" Depth: $4^3/4$" Height: $4^3/4$"
Sculpted very quickly (in a few days) after a suggestion made by John Hine one evening in the pub.
MARKINGS: Guild No. 5 © David Winter 1988
ISSUE PRICE: £46 $105
CURRENT VALUE: £100 – 200 $200 – 250
UPDATE: _____

THE COAL SHED

SCULPTED: 1989
LOCATION: Home Studio
RETIRED: 1991
SIZE: Width: $7^3/4$" Depth: $4^1/4$" Height: $4^1/2$"
The Coal Shed is an accurate model of the place where the first David Winter Cottages were made, namely David's parents' coalshed. The metal roof is detachable and inside are the figures of John Hine (talking in the phone) and David Winter (sculpting). There's a particularly delightful mouse, too, or rather half-a-mouse . . . if you can find it!
MARKINGS: Guild No. 6 © David Winter 1989
ISSUE PRICE: £50 $112
CURRENT VALUE: £150 – 220 $250 – 300
UPDATE: _____

THE PLUCKED DUCKS

SCULPTED: 1989
LOCATION: Home Studio
RETIRED: 1990
SIZE: Width: 7" Height: $5^1/4$"
The free Guild Membership piece for 1990. A flat-backed piece in a rectangular shadow box.
MARKINGS: © David Winter 1989
ISSUE PRICE: £ NIL $ NIL
CURRENT VALUE: £70 – 90 $120 – 220
UPDATE: _____

THE COBBLER
SCULPTED: 1989
LOCATION: Home Studio
SIZE: Width: 2 $^5/_8$" Depth: 2 $^1/_2$" Height: 3"
The 1990 Guild pieces were made small to complement the largish models of previous years.
MARKINGS: Guild No. 7 © David Winter 1989
ISSUE PRICE: £15 $40
UPDATE: _____

THE POTTERY
SCULPTED: 1989
LOCATION: Home Studio
SIZE: Width: 3 $^1/_2$" Depth: 2" Height: 2 $^3/_4$"
MARKINGS: Guild No. 8 © David Winter 1989
ISSUE PRICE: £15 $40
UPDATE: _____

PERSHORE MILL
SCULPTED: 1990
LOCATION: Home Studio
RETIRED: 1991
SIZE: Width: 6 $^1/_2$" Height: 6 $^1/_2$"
The free Guild Membership piece for 1991 – a flat-backed piece in a hexagonal shadow box. John Hine grew up in Pershore and knew the real Pershore Mill very well. It burned down some thirty years ago and was never rebuilt. David's piece is entirely imaginary and inspired John to write his book The Tale of Pershore Mill, a story set in the 18th century using photographs of real people set against illustrated backgrounds. All the characters are played by members of John Hine Studios, including David Winter and John Hine.
MARKINGS: © David Winter 1990
ISSUE PRICE: £NIL $NIL
CURRENT VALUE: Unknown
UPDATE: _____

TOMFOOL'S COTTAGE
SCULPTED: 1990
LOCATION: Home Studio
RELEASED: 1991
SIZE: Width: 4 $^3/_4$" Depth: 4 $^1/_8$" Height 5 $^1/_4$"
MARKINGS: Guild No. 9 © David Winter 1990
ISSUE PRICE: £35 $100
UPDATE: _____

WILL-'O-THE-WISP
SCULPTED: 1991
LOCATION: Home Studio
SIZE: Width: 6 $^1/_2$" Depth: 3 $^1/_2$" Height: 6 $^1/_4$"
MARKINGS: Guild No. 10 © David Winter 1991
ISSUE PRICE: £55 $120
UPDATE: _____

IRISH WATER MILL
SCULPTED: 1991
LOCATION: Home Studio
RELEASED: 1992
SIZE: Width: 3 $^7/_8$" Depth: 2 $^7/_8$" Height: 2 $^5/_8$"
The free Guild Membership piece for 1992. Current until 31st December 1992.
MARKINGS: © David Winter 1991
ISSUE PRICE: £NIL $NIL
UPDATE: _____

THE BEEKEEPER'S
SCULPTED: 1991
LOCATION: Home Studio
RELEASED: 1992
SIZE: Width: 3" Depth: 2 $^3/_4$" Height: 5 $^3/_4$"
REMARKS: Current until 31st December 1992.
MARKINGS: © David Winter 1991
ISSUE PRICE: £34 $65
UPDATE: _____

THE CANDLEMAKER'S
SCULPTED: 1991
LOCATION: Home Studio
RELEASED: 1992
SIZE: Width: 4 $^1/_8$" Depth: 3 $^1/_2$" Height: 4 $^1/_2$"
Current until 31st December 1992.
MARKINGS: © David Winter 1991
ISSUE PRICE: £34 $65
UPDATE: _____

8 - PIECES NEVER RELEASED

David Winter is not the kind of artist who produces a mass of work and then chooses to release only a percentage for production. He is a frugal and economical worker, and a mere handful of Cottages exist that have never been released. In addition there are a few 'odd' pieces which have come to light and are listed here.

19 ASH STREET

When an extension was planned for the garage at 19 Ash Street premises near Aldershot, David sculpted a model of how John Hine wanted it to look. Instead of presenting plans to the local Planning Department for permission to go ahead, John submitted the model! In his words: "They were not amused" – and permission was refused. The model is now in John's possession. For a while he used it as a door stop!

THE LIGHTHOUSE

SCULPTED: 1990

The Lighthouse was sculpted as part of the Irish Collection before David stopped work on it in 1990. He wasn't happy with this piece whilst sculpting it, nor was he satisfied with the end result – an opinion perhaps reflected by the inclusion of a helicopter pad with a large 'H' (a very un-David Winter-like feature!). It almost had a new lease of life as a special Guild piece (hence the markings), but this was nothing more than a passing consideration.

SIZE: Width: 4" Depth: 3 ^{3}/4" Height 7 ^{1}/2"

MARKINGS: Guild No. 10 © David Winter 1990

O'REILLY'S BAR

SCULPTED: 1989

One of the first pieces David sculpted for the Irish Collection, but it didn't make it into the four released in 1992. Some were painted as test pieces, although none seems to have survived. The example here is of undipped, unpainted Crystacal.

SIZE: Width: 5" Depth: 3 ^{1}/2" Height: 3 ^{1}/2"

MARKINGS: © David Winter 1989

AN IRISH COTTAGE

David half-completed a piece for the Irish collection, described by him as "just an Irish cottage". However it was never finished and ended up back in his wax melter.

PHONEBOX

Very early on David sculpted a typical British telephone box, but this didn't even make it beyond the wax stage. For a long time it hung around the coal shed and nothing ever came of it. Its whereabouts is currently unknown.

WILLIAM SHAKESPEARE DEATHPLACE

A piece David made as a joke to parody all the various sizes of William Shakespeare's Birthplace that were being made at one time. It consisted of a small plot of land with a single tombstone marked R.I.P.! None are known to exist.

VILLAGE SCENE WITH BACK

SCULPTED: 1986

LOCATION: 19 Ash Street, but the back was added at David's Home Studio.

When the Village Scene piece was being adapted from a Point of Sale into the free 1987/88 Guild piece, several attempts were made to alleviate the problem of the spire which protrudes from the top. It often snapped off during demoulding and even if it survived production was easily broken. One solution was a sheet of cardboard cut to the shape of the piece and glued to the back. Another experiment was this piece – the Village Scene with a flat rectangular back to it, all cast in a single mould from Crystacal. Neither of these ideas was implemented and Village Scene remained as it was, and it remains a delicate piece.

The example photographed for this book is in John Hine's possession.

MARKINGS: © David Winter 1986

19 Ash Street

The Lighthouse, (The accompanying Round Tower gives an indication of size)

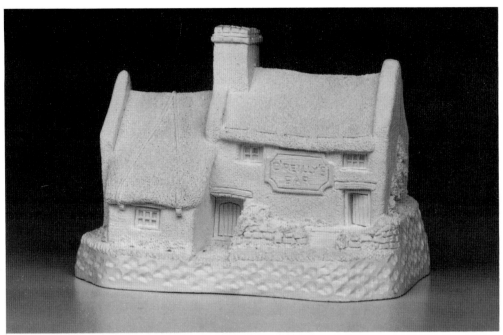

O'Reilly's Bar

Village Scene with back

9 - THE MOUSE

YES! David Winter does sculpt a tiny mouse on his pieces. BUT! It's not on all of them, sometimes it is very indistinct, and on later versions of certain pieces (such as Snow Cottage) it may have worn off in the mould.

The first piece to have a mouse was Brookside Hamlet, so please do not hold your breath trying to find it on pieces sculpted prior to that!

Whilst David was sculpting Brookside Hamlet, another artist who then worked for John Hine Studios had sculpted a series of animals, and one of them was a mouse sitting on a piece of cheese. David claimed that it looked more like a rat and proceeded to sculpt a little mouse on the piece he was working on to show what a mouse should look like. It stayed there . . . . and so the mouse began.

At the time he wasn't aware that others have done this before. The artist Terence Cuneo signs his paintings with a mouse, and Yorkshire furniture makers R. Thompsons sculpt a mouse on all their products (the founder Robert Thompsons started it in the 1930s when he sculpted a mouse on a church beam).

John Hine Studios have never admitted that a mouse exists, and their stock-in-trade-answer to the enquiry has always been: "MOUSE? WHAT MOUSE?". The non-existent mouse has thus acquired a name of sorts – What Mouse. Instead there have been some very unsubtle hints: a chapter in John Hine's book Collecting David Winter Cottages called The Mouse in which the only words are "Mouse? What Mouse?" and a tail disappearing off the page; a section of Cottage Country called "Squeak!!!" with the same mouse tail; a Toby Jug of David Winter sitting back to back with a huge sleepy mouse.

Then there is *The Great Mouse Hunt*, a competition for Guild Members with clues running through issues of 'Cottage Country' from Summer 1991 to Spring 1992. The prize is a valuable solid gold mouse sculpted by David Winter's talented sister Alice.

Is this the nearest there will ever be to a confession? Is it the culmination of the mouse saga? I'm sorry, I haven't a clue! The mouse seems to be still around: there's a splendid example on CASTLE IN THE AIR.

When David remodelled early pieces after he had sculpted Brookside Hamlet, he did not then include the mouse. Also some very early examples of certain models are mouseless because David forgot to put it on – and did so when production had already begun.

The mouse is the last detail that David sculpts on a new piece.

The fun of hunting for the mouse on David Winter Cottages would be spoiled by listing their wherabouts. However a photograph of one might help some collectors at least to know what they are looking for! This particular rodent can be found on **The Boat House**. See page 102.

10 - SECONDARY MARKET TABLE (AT A GLANCE)

NAME	ISSUE PRICE		CURRENT VALUE	
	U.K.	U.S..	U.K..	U.S.
	£	$	£	$
ANNE HATHAWAY'S COTTAGE	2	*	300 – 500	1000– 1500
THE ALMS HOUSES	22	60	250–400	500–750
BLACK BESS INN	25	60	150–250	180–300
BLACKSMITH'S COTTAGE	6	22	125–175	450–650
BOTTLE KILN	28	78	45–50	85–90
BROOKSIDE HAMLET	23	75	50–60	100–130
CASTLE KEEP	7	*	750–1,000	2000–2500
(with Guildford Castle plaque)			1000+	2500+
CARTWRIGHT'S COTTAGE	35	45	75–125	120–250
CHICHESTER CROSS	17	*	1300–1500	3400–3800
(If perfect)			2500+	6000+
CHICHESTER CROSS (bronze)	45	*	5000+	10,000+
A CHRISTMAS CAROL	46	135	80–120	140–180
CHRISTMAS IN SCOTLAND AND HOGMANAY	46	100	75–150	150–200
THE COACHING INN	36	165	1500–2500	4500–6000
THE COAL SHED	50	112	150–220	250–300
CORNISH COTTAGE	8	30	400–600	1300–1900
CORNISH TIN MINE	7	22	50–75	75–125
COTSWOLD FARMHOUSE	2	*	300–500	1000–1,500
COTSWOLD VILLAGE	20	60	50–60	85–110
COTTON MILL	14	42	300–400	800–1000
CROFTER'S COTTAGE	17	51	40–70	75–120
CROWN INN	2	*	300–500	1000–1500
DOUBLE OAST	10	*	1500–1800	4000–5000
DOVE COTTAGE	7.50	60	650–900	1800–2400
EBENEZER SCROOGE'S COUNTING HOUSE	42	97	175–250	220–300
FAIRYTALE CASTLE	40	115	125–200	150–250
FALSTAFF'S MANOR	115	242	200–300	350–550
THE FORGE	9	60	650–850	2300–3000
FRED'S HOME	60	145	65–70	150–160
THE GRANGE	60	120	650–1000	1200–2000
THE HAYBARN	6	22	100–150	400–600
HERMITS HUMBLE HOME	32	87	200–250	200–300
HOME GUARD	46	105	100 –200	200–250
HOUSE OF THE MASTER MASON	32	75	150–200	250–300
HOUSE ON TOP	32	92	200–250	250–350
LITTLE FORGE	4.50	40	700–1000	2100–2900

NAME	ISSUE PRICE		CURRENT VALUE	
	U.K.	U.S..	U.K..	U.S.
	£	$	£	$
LITTLE MILL (original)	4.50	*	1500–1750	2300–3200
LITTLE MILL (mark 2)	4.50	40	1000–1300	1900–2500
LITTLE MILL (mark 3)	4.50	40	900–1100	1700–2300
MILL HOUSE (original)	7.50	*	1500–2000	2500–3000
MILL HOUSE (restyled)	7.50	50	1000–1250	1900–2600
MINER'S COTTAGE	6	22	100–150	300–450
MISTER FEZZIWIG'S EMPORIUM	60	135	75–90	135–180
MOORLAND COTTAGE	6	22	100–150	250–350
THE OLD CURIOSITY SHOP	10	40	600–800	1800–2400
ORCHARD COTTAGE	42	91	60–80	125–150
THE PAVILION	23	52	150–220	200–300
PERSHORE MILL	NIL	NIL	*	*
THE PLUCKED DUCKS	NIL	NIL	70–90	120–220
PROVENCAL ONE	7.50	*	5000+	15,000+
PROVENCAL TWO	7.50	*	8000+	15000+
PROVENCAL A (Tiny)	3	*	750–950	1600–2400
PROVENCAL B (Tiny)	3	*	750–950	1600–2400
QUAYSIDE	9	60	750–950	1700–2300
QUEEN ELIZABETH SLEPT HERE	70	183	200–300	400–550
ROBIN HOOD'S HIDEAWAY	18	54	250–350	350–550
SABRINA'S COTTAGE	5.50	*	1000–1300	2500–3000
ST. NICHOLAS' CHURCH	2	*	300–500	1300–1800
ST. PAUL'S CATHEDRAL	9	*	700–900	2500–2800
SPINNER'S COTTAGE	9	27	25–40	50–80
SQUIRES HALL	37	92	70–80	130–150
STREET SCENE (Bas Relief Plaque)	NIL	NIL	100–150	150–250
SUFFOLK HOUSE	22	49	50–100	80–130
SULGRAVE MANOR	2	*	300–500	1000–1500
THREE DUCKS INN	7.50	*	800–1000	2600–2900
TUDOR MANOR HOUSE	6	47	50–75	100–200
TYTHE BARN (door on)	11	39	900–1100	2000–2600
TYTHE BARN (door off)	11	39	700–850	1600–2000
VILLAGE SCENE (Collectors' Guild)	NIL	NIL	100–150	250–450
VILLAGE SCENE (Point of Sale)	NIL	NIL	150–200	300–500
WINTERSHILL (Jim'll Fix It)	200	375	1500–2000	4000–6500
WILLIAM SHAKESPEARE'S BIRTHPLACE (large)	23	60	500–800	1800–2300
WILLIAM SHAKESPEARE'S BIRTHPLACE (Tiny)	2	*	300–500	1000–1500
WOODCUTTERS COTTAGE	33	87	200–250	250–350

11 - DAVID WINTER MEMORABILIA

Listed here is published material, promotional items and miscellaneous David Winter 'offshoots', which apart from one item (the David Winter Toby Jug) have all been produced by John Hine Studios.

COLLECTING DAVID WINTER COTTAGES
by John Hine
In his own inimitable style John Hine set down in 1989 a compendium of information essential to the avid collector of David Winter Cottages. He explains from a personal point of view how the whole idea of the Cottages developed, the achievements of the first ten years, and his feelings about his collaboration with David Winter. There are also fascinating thumbnail sketches of all the pieces in the current range – often revealing, sometimes funny, sometimes touching; and always fascinating. From cover to cover it is a jolly good read!
Collecting David Winter Cottages is still currently available, also in a special leather bound edition.

THE COLLECTORS BOOK
First published in 1985, The Collectors Book was reprinted in a slightly different and updated format as *The Collectors Catalogue* until it disappeared from print in 1989. It was a pocket-sized book containing illustrations of the pieces available at the time with brief write-ups, not unlike the ones that are found in the box with every David Winter Cottage.
The Collectors Book proved very popular with collectors and many copies were sold, although it became very out-of-date towards the end of its run.

COLLECTORS POCKET BOOK
Produced at the same time as John Hine's Collecting David Winter Cottages in 1989, the Collectors Pocket Book is a soft-covered, 60-page booklet containing photographs and descriptive pieces about all the current range, up to and including the British Traditions Collection. The cover has a brown wood effect design which was also used on a thin brochure in the same year.

CARDS
A catalogue of David Winter Cottages in the form of a pack of cards was produced at one stage, and from the pieces contained therein it can be dated to 1984. On one side of the cards is a photograph of a piece and on the other a short explanatory narrative. Each pack contains 40 cards, including a biography of David Winter and a fascinating photograph of him at work sculpting Castle Gate. The piece in the picture is very different from the final version!
A special Point of Sale was made to display the cards, incorporating sculpture work by David Winter. It was a fragile item and the cards did not stand well in the slots provided, but it too is collected and has developed a value on the secondary market.

ISSUE PRICE:	£1.50	$5
CURRENT PRICE:	£40 – 50	$100 – 150

RETIRED RANGE RING BINDER
A hardback file produced in 1989 containing loose-leaf photographs of all the retired pieces. A new set of additional sheets were produced on 1990, however no further updates have since been made.

TABLE MATS & COASTERS
A set of table mats and coasters were made for John Hine Studios by the Clover Leaf company in London featuring colour illustrations of six David Winter Cottages – The Bothy, Tudor Manor House, Sussex Cottage, Stratford House, The Bakehouse and The Dower House. The same pieces appeared on both the table mats and coasters. They were first released in August 1984 and the last orders were placed with Clover Leaf by John Hine Studios in late 1985, so they probably remained available in shops well into 1986. A plan to re-order the same sets again in 1991 was abandoned when it was realised that this would affect the value of the originals on the secondary market. A second set with illustrations of different pieces has been discussed instead and there is a chane that this might see the light of day during 1992.

TABLE MATS (Set of 6)
ISSUE PRICE:	£10	$30
CURRENT PRICE:	£75 – 100	$200-300

COASTERS (Set of 6)
ISSUE PRICE:	£8	$13
CURRENT PRICE:	£50 – 75	$75-100

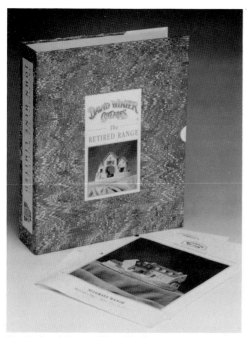

The Retired Range Ring Binder

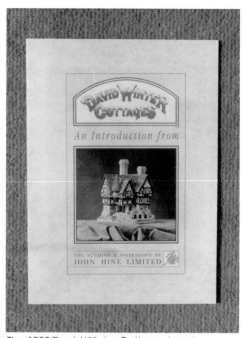

The 1988 David Winter Cottages brochure

An early brochure dating from 1981

THE GUILD PIPE & SMOKING ACCESSORIES

A pipe, specially blended tobacco, leather pouch and pipe rack, all embossed with the word GUILD, were made to accompany an article about pipe smoking for issue No.4 (Winter '87) of Cottage Country magazine. Only small numbers of each were made.

ISSUE PRICES:	
PIPE	£32/$50.00;
TOBACCO (per tin)	£3.50/$6.00;
POUCH	£27.00/$43.00;
PIPE RACK	£90/$145.00.
CURRENT PRICES:	Unknown.

DAVID WINTER ROCK

Two hundred sticks of traditional British seaside rock (cylindrical rods of candy about a foot in length) with 'David Winter' written through the middle were made for a feature in issue No. 6 (Summer '88) of Cottage Country. They were produced mainly to demonstrate how rock is made, and were offered as a free gift to contributors to Cottage Country's Letters Page and Collectors Marketplace. Sticks of rock were duly dispatched to Guild members for about a year. Remaining stocks were then deemed inedible and thrown away.

DAVID WINTER TOBY JUG

Toby Jug manufacturers Kevin Francis Ceramics of London approached John Hine Studios in the autumn of 1990 with the idea of including David Winter in their series of Tobies entitled Great Artists and Potters (others include Clarice Cliff, Hannah Barlow, Suzy Cooper and Josiah Wedgwood). David was flattered to be included amongst such distinguished company and readily agreed. The piece was sculpted by Doug Tootle from Stoke-On-Trent and depicts David holding The Dower House and sitting on Blossom Cottage (with the chimney thoughfully moved to one side!). A limited edition of 950 were produced, and although this has officially sold out, a small number have been reserved for visitors to the new in-house shop at Eggars Hill..

ISSUE PRICE:	£250	$450
CURRENT PRICE:	£350-450	$900-1,200

'MEET THE ARTIST' VIDEO

This 30-minute video is a fascinating insight into how David Winter sculpts, with much footage of him at work in his studio and some revealing comments on the soundtrack by David himself. It was produced during the summer of 1990 and he can be seen at work on Mr. Fezziwig's Emporium.

Also to be seen are Pershore Mill and 'Fred's Home...', which were in the process of being sculpted. John Hine is also featured, plus various collectors talking about their pieces and how they feel about David's work.

PROMOTIONAL MATERIAL

A variety of brochures and booklets have been published by John Hine Studios, and it is possible to date them by the Cottages featured within.

1980 *David Winter Cottages.* Small cream booklet (4" x 3"), four sheets stapled, featuring line drawings of pieces from Mill House (restyled but not the original) to Quayside, plus Provencal One and Two. The Coaching Inn is mentioned but not illustrated. On the front is a portrait of David sculpting, drawn by his sister Alice.

1981 *David Winter Cottages.* A single cream sheet folded to A5- size with illustrations of '34 miniature cottages evoking the spirit of rural life from days gone by.'. It was presumably released towards the end of the year as it features The Village as 'David Winter's special piece for Christmas 1981.'.

1982/3 A single A4-size sheet folded in half.

1984 *Flights of Fancy. David Winter Cottages – The Collection.* A single A5-size white folded sheet featuring colour illustrations of 35 pieces. Some 1984 pieces are included (e.g. Castle Gate, The Parsonage) whilst others are not (Snow Cottage, Tollkeeper's Cottage).

1985 *David Winter Cottages – The Collection.* Same format as *Flights of Fancy* only with a brown background instead of white, and dated 1985. Features 45 pieces plus the 10 new Heart of England pieces.

1986 *David Winter Cottages – The Collection.* Pale blue cover with map of Great Britain, five stapled sheets, photographs set against illustrations of craftsmen at work. A different craftsman is highlighted on each double-page spread. Produced in 1986, but the only piece sculpted in that year to be featured is Falstaff's Manor.

1988 *David Winter Cottages – An introduction from John Hine Studios.* Has a picture of Falstaff's Manor on the front.

1988 *David Winter Cottages – Fine English Collectibles.* Single sheet folding out to A3-size, with a dark purple front featuring Lacemakers. Contains photographs of pieces then current, with all 1988 pieces including The Grange. Produced by John Hine Studios in the U.S.A.

1989 *David Winter Cottages – Finest Miniature Houses.* A5-size with a dark brown, wood effect cover similar to the Collectors Pocket Book; six sheets stapled with a fold-out back page displaying the main Collection. Also produced in several languages for the European market.

1991 *David Winter Cottages.* A stapled, landscape format booklet with a pale blue cover. First released in February at a trade show in Birmingham and then revised before general release.

BOXES AND CERTIFICATES

BOXES

For over a year David Winter Cottages were sold unboxed, wrapped in tissue paper and without a box or a Certificate of Authenticity. If a box was requested by a customer, it was probably improvised — a shoebox or something similar. Since boxes became part of standard production procedure, various styles have been used, in the following order: (Dates are approximate and apply to production only; stocks in shops and stores would remain in the old boxes for some time after a change of style.)

1 April 1981 — March 1985: Plain brown. (Still used for large pieces.)

2 March 1985 — October 1986: Mottled dark brown/green or plain white. (Plain white were used for sizes of box that could not be supplied in the mottled brown/green design. Plain white boxes are still occasionally used for small and medium-sized pieces, as they are for other John Hine Studio artists.

3 October 1986 onwards: Light blue, red or yellow tint with village characters and scenes illustrated around the sides. This design is currently the standard box for David Winter Cottages.

CUSTOMISED BOXES

St.Paul's Cathedral had a special wrap-around sleeve to commemorate the Royal Wedding of 1981. Apart from this, no special box designs were used until the 1989 Christmas piece, A Christmas Carol, which had a photograph of the piece in a seasonal setting printed onto the box. The two subsequent Christmas pieces, Mr. Fezziwig's Emporium (1990) and Fred's Home — "Merry Christmas, Uncle Ebenezer," said Scrooge's nephew Fred, "and a Happy New Year" (1991) have followed suit, and presumably the 1992 piece will continue the trend.

CASTLE IN THE AIR is the first (and so far only) piece in the Collection to have a fully-illustrated box, presumably due to the prestige status of the piece. Extending this aspect of packaging may well be a theme for the future.

Curiously, previous prestige pieces such as The Parsonage, The Old Distillery and Smugglers Creek have never had any specialised packaging, and even today they are delivered in plain brown cardboard boxes.

INSIDE THE BOX

The protective packaging inside 'David Winter' boxes has taken three forms over the years:
1 Tissue paper.
2 Bubble-wrap and/or polystyrene chunks (snow).
3 Two specially moulded foam cushions.

CERTIFICATES OF AUTHENTICITY

Certificates of Authenticity were introduced in late 1984 and ever since then one has been inserted in the box with every David Winter Cottage, usually with a brief descriptive narrative about the piece. As the company grew in size, a change in the wording became necessary to reflect the fact that John Hine and David Winter were no longer able to supervise personally the production of all models.

Original wording: We hereby certify that this piece is an authentic David Winter Cottage, hand-made and hand-painted at the Studio and Workshops of John Hine Limited, Woolmer Way, Bordon, Hampshire, England, under the personal supervision of David Winter and John Hine.

Revised wording: We hereby certify that this piece is an authentic David Winter Cottage, hand-made and hand-painted at the Studio and Workshops of John Hine Limited, Woolmer Way, Bordon, Hampshire, England, under the guidance of David Winter and John Hine.

A selection of David Winter Cottage boxes

12 - NEW FOR 1992

Inevitably this book will be out-of-date as soon as it is printed, as new decisions affecting pieces are constantly being made within John Hine Studios, and seems to have reached a prolific period in his creative life. Who knows what he will come up with in the next few months! However, listed here are all new items planned for 1992 as at 31st December 1991. The three standard Guild pieces for 1992 (Irish Water Mill, The Beekeeper's, The Candlemaker's) are featured in Chapter Six.

AUDREY'S TEA ROOM

SCULPTED: 1991
RELEASED: 1992
LOCATION: Home Studio
RETIRED: 1992
SIZE: Length: 3 ^{5}/8" Depth 3 ^{1}/4" Height: 3 ^{1}/4"
The name is a tribute to Audrey White, first ever painter of David Winter Cottages, who retired during 1991. For several years Audrey painted at Eggars Hill and was a familiar face to collectors who came to tour John Hine Studios. She also features in the video *Meet the Artist* in which she is seen with David Winter and John Hine originating the colours for Mr Fezziwig's Emporium. A few of the first pieces to be released had the erroneous name, 'Audrey's Tea Shop' on the base label.

No sooner had this piece appeared than it was withdrawn again on 26th March 1992 as a result of a lorry fire in which the master moulds were being transported. The production run can only have been brief, and quantities produced must be considerably lower than even The Grange. The secondary market value will escalate rapidly during 1992 and Audrey's Tea Room is currently very collectable. If you can find one, buy it!
MARKINGS: © David Winter 1991
UPDATE: _____

THE IRISH COLLECTION

SCULPTED: 1990/91
LOCATION: Home Studio and Ireland
An Irish collection to complement the Heart of England, West Country, Midlands and Scottish collections has always been on the cards, and in *Cottage Country* No. 8 (Winter '88) it was scheduled for release in 1990. Then in No. 13 (Spring '90) a postponement until the following summer was announced, but superseded in No. 16 (Winter '90) by an *indefinite* postponement.

Two factors were involved in the delay: firstly, John Hine was keen to try and have th pieces actually made in Ireland, which when investigated proved a great deal more difficult than anticipated; secondly, although pleased with some of his work on the project, David Winter was dissatisfied with the collection as a whole and abandoned work on it until 1991 when he was able to look at it afresh.

SECRET SHEBEEN

SCULPTED: 1991
An entirely new piece sculpted in 1991. A shebeen is an illicit drinking house, where the infamous and highly potent poteen is distilled and consumed behing closed doors.
SIZE: Length 5 ^{1}/2" Depth: 4 ^{1}/8" Height 4 ^{1}/4"
MARKINGS: © David Winter 1991

ONLY A SPAN APART

SCULPTED: 1990/91
A lovely piece consisting of two cottages linked by a bridge over a small river. When the first Irish Collection was put on hold, this was considered as a possible special Guild piece for 1991, but that idea too was shelved. For a long time this piece had the working title, Bridge to Peace.

FOGARTYS

SCULPTED 1990/91
A piece which reflects the distinctive *Irish bar* as opposed to the *British pub*.
SIZE: Length: 5 ^{1}/2" Depth 3 ^{3}/4" Height 3 ^{7}/8"
MARKINGS: © David Winter 1991

IRISH ROUND TOWER

SCULPTED 1990/91
Although sculpted for the original Irish Collection, Irish Round Tower never got beyond the resin and master stage. David made some alterations to it before allowing it to become part of the new Irish Collection. This is David's favourite of all the original pieces and he has the resin master in his cottage in Ireland.
SIZE: Width: 5" Depth: 3 ^{3}/4" Height 4 ^{1}/4"
MARKINGS © David Winter 1991

CAMEOS
SCULPTED: 1991

Twelve very small miniatures, all less than 2" in width, depth and height. As the name suggests, they depict specific details from village life rather than actual dwellings. Cameos can be purchased to be free standing or for display on a separate diorama, also sculpted by David Winter. For a very short time the diorama was available in light or bright colours, but the bright version soon proved to be the more popular of the two. The light version was retired on 26th March 1992. Its value on the secondary market will no doubt rise rapidly.

The Cameos are

POULTRY ARK	BARLEY MALT KILN
MARKET DAY	LYCH GATE
BROOKLET BRIDGE	SADDLE STEPS
PENNY WISHING WELL	ONE MAN JAIL
THE POTTING SHED	THE PRIVY
GREENWOOD WAGON	WELSH PIG PEN

LIMITED TIME EDITION PIECE
This is a new venture for David Winter Cottages, a piece available only for a limited time — from mid June to mid July 1992. The edition will then be closed and its size announced. The piece may well be the first of several pieces made available to collectors this way.

As this book goes to print, the name and details of the piece have not yet been released but a space has been left for them to be added.

NAME: _____

DETAILS: _____

_____

_____

_____

1992 CHRISTMAS PIECE
Details of the 1992 Christmas piece have not yet been released but it will be another in the series inspired by Charles Dickens' A Christmas Carol. Again, space is left for the details to be added when available.:

NAME: _____

DETAILS: _____

_____

_____

_____

Cameos on a lightly painted (now retired) diorama. The darkly painted diorama is still current

Audrey's Tea Room, front and back

Only a Span Apart (L) and Secret Shebeen

Fogartys (L) and Irish Round Tower

13- SPECIAL COMMISSION AND CHARITY PIECES

Two pieces have been released in limited editions specifically to raise money for charity (Wintershill and Cartwright's Cottage), and another two (CASTLE IN THE AIR and Gatekeepers) have been adapted for charitable purposes. Listed here also is Green Lanes — the only private commission David has ever undertaken.

WINTERSHILL (Jim'll Fix It)
SCULPTED: 1987
LOCATION: Home Studio
RETIRED: 1988
SIZE: Width: 4" Depth: 3 $^3/_4$" Height 4 $^1/_8$"
This piece was made in a limited edition of 250 to raise money for the Great Ormond Street Hospital for Children's Wishing Well Appeal. It sold initially for £200 or US$375 and raised £50,000 towards the rebuilding of London's world famous hospital. The idea stemmed from Jody Jackman, whose mother Penny is a keen collector of 'David Winters'. In 1987 Jody, then aged 10, wrote to the BBC's Jim'll Fix It programme to ask if her mother could see how a David Winter Cottage is made. Not only was her request granted but David chose to sculpt the Jackman's home in Framlington, Hampshire, specially for the programme. The show's host, Sir Jimmy Saville OBE, is renowned for his charity work, so the limited edition idea with the proceeds going to the Wishing Well Appeal was a natural progression. The idea was announced on the actual show itself, which was broadcast on 27th February 1988.
The name Wintershill was invented for the piece, but the Jackmans have since christened their own house with the same name.
MARKINGS: © David Winter 1987
ISSUE PRICE: £200 $375
CURRENT VALUE: £1,500 – 2,000 $4,000 – 6,500
UPDATE: _____

CARTWRIGHT'S COTTAGE
SCULPTED: 1988
RELEASED: 1990
LOCATION: Home Studio
RETIRED: 1990
SIZE: Width: 4" Depth: 2 $^3/_4$" Height 3 $^1/_2$"
Although sculpted in 1988, Cartwright's Cottage was not released until Spring 1990 when a limited edition was produced to raise money for the U.S.-based Ronald McDonald Children's Charities. In July 1990, at the International Plate & Collectible Show at South Bend, Indiana, a cheque for $225,000 was presented to R.M.C.C., and in addition at least $10,000 have since been forwarded to them.
The piece was not named until late 1989, and for two years it was known to many as 'Lynne', after Lynne Kentish who was then a member of John Hine Studios.
MARKINGS: © David Winter 1988
ISSUE PRICE: £35 $45
CURRENT VALUE: £75 – 125 $120 – 250
UPDATE: _____

CASTLE IN THE AIR (BRONZE)
To commemorate the London Collectors Showcase, held in London in October 1991, a cold cast bronze version of CASTLE IN THE AIR was cast as a prize for the show's Silent Auction, in which bids were written down during the course of the day with the last bidder before a cut-off time being the winner. In a flurry of activity in tha last few seconds, this unique piece was sold for £2,600.
The technique for making it was the same used in the bronze Chichester Cross – a 30% resin/70% bronze powder mix.
The actual piece itself is identical to the normal painted version of CASTLE IN THE AIR.

GATEKEEPER'S (COLOURWAY)
For the same show as the bronze CASTLE IN THE AIR, a colourway of Gatekeeper's from the Scottish Collection was painted in a limited edition of 1,000. Proceeds of the sale have been given to Haylands Farm, at Ryde on the Isle of Wight, which is part of Mencap.
On this colourway of Gatekeeper's, the roof is reddish-brown and slightly textured, with some tiles darker than others, whilst the normal production piece has grey tiles. This is the only difference.
ISSUE PRICE: £65. $N/A.

Special Commissions / Charity Pieces

GREEN LANES
SCULPTED: 1980
LOCATION: The Coalshed
SIZE: Width: 8" Depth: 3" Height: 3"

Nicholas Rink is a friend of David Winter's – a fellow regular at his local pub – who commissioned a sculpture of his house, Green Lanes, as a Christmas present. The work was done in a great hurry, being completed only on Christmas Eve. David used a single rubber block mould and cast it himself. John Hine took it home with him and left it on his storage heater overnight to dry. Then John actually painted it himself, sitting at Faith Winter's dining room table. As soon as it was ready, they rushed down to the pub to deliver it to Mr. Rink. This is David Winter's one-and-only private commission. Only one model was cast and the mould was destroyed in the process. Consequently it must rank as the rarest of all completed cottages by David Winter.

The bronze CASTLE IN THE AIR

Wintershill (Jim'll Fix It) and Cartwright's Cottage

Green Lanes, the only private commission David Winter has ever undertaken

Green Lanes, rear view

Gatekeepers in its colourway (left) and conventional colours

Is this a mouse I see before me? Yes, creeping along the side of the boat house

14- RARITIES

several items by David Winter need to be listed apart from the 'retired' Cottages as they never made it into the Collection. Nevertheless they have been available for purchase at some stage or another. Some occasionally appear on the secondary market, whilst others have no track record to date.

CARD DISPENSER
SCULPTED: 1984
LOCATION: Home Studio
RETIRED: 1984
SIZE: Width: 10" Depth: 4 $^{1}/_{2}$" Height 8 $^{1}/_{2}$"
This was produced as a Point of Sale for shops to display the Collectors' Catalogue Cards. It was sculpted slightly after the cards were released, and David made it in two parts which were glued together. Very few are now in existence.
MARKINGS: None

ISSUE PRICE:	NIL	$ NIL
CURRENT VALUE:	Unknown	$ 5,000.00
UPDATE:	_____	

CHICHESTER CROSS (BRONZE)
SCULPTED: 1981
LOCATION: 19 Ash Street
RETIRED: 1981
SIZE: Width: 3 $^{1}/_{2}$"
Depth: 3 $^{1}/_{2}$" Height 4 $^{1}/_{4}$"
A limited edition (6 only) of Chichester Cross using a bronze/resin mix was cast for an exhibition at The Maltings, Farnham, of work by artists from David's village (of whom there are several). David Winter cast just one for display and five more were subsequently produced to fulfill orders taken at the exhibition.
MARKINGS: None

ISSUE PRICE:	45	$N/A
CURRENT VALUE:	5,000+	$10,000+
UPDATE:	_____	

COACHING INN (CANDLEHOLDER BASE)
SCULPTED: 1980
LOCATION: The Coalshed.
RETIRED: 1980
SIZE: Width: 15 $^{1}/_{2}$" Depth: 11" Height 2 $^{1}/_{2}$"
An optional extra for The Coaching Inn. This consists of a stand with a hollow centre on which the piece rests. Around the edge are sockets for holding candles. The Coaching Inn was finished towards the end of 1980 and the candleholder base was made as an attraction for the Christmas period only. Few of them were sold and the piece is now very rare. Unusually, David sculpted the original not in wax but plasticine.
MARKINGS: None

ISSUE PRICE:	Unknown	$ Unknown
CURRENT VALUE:	Unknown	$ Unknown
UPDATE:	_____	

STRATFORD HOUSE (TERRACOTTA)
SCULPTED: 1981
LOCATION: 19 Ash Street
RETIRED: 1981
SIZE: Width: 6 $^{1}/_{4}$" Depth: 4" Height 4 $^{5}/_{8}$"
A limited edition of Stratford House in terracotta was cast for the same exhibition as the bronze Chichester Cross. Only two are known to exist; Faith Winter owns the display model, marked Number One on the base, and the other is in a private collection in the U.S.A. Another may have been sold at the exhibition, but no one can remember for certain, and no records exist. David cast them himself from the original master mould, which is a solid block of inflexible silicon rubber, very different from skin-like production moulds. Demoulding Crystacal from them isn't easy, and he was bet by a colleague that he couldn't demould Number One intact. David won the bet.
MARKINGS: David Winter

ISSUE PRICE:	Unknown
CURRENT VALUE:	Unknown
UPDATE	_____

VILLAGE SCENE (POINT OF SALE)
SCULPTED: 1986
LOCATION: 19 Ash Street
SIZE: Width: 6 $^{1}/_{2}$" Depth: 4 $^{5}/_{8}$" Height 4 $^{3}/_{4}$"
The free Guild Membership piece for 1987 and '88 was an adaptation of this Point of Sale, previously available to David Winter Cottage's authorised stockists. The only difference between the two is the wording on the oval plaque. The Guild piece reads David Winter Cottages Collectors Guild and the Point of Sale reads David Winter Cottages. Although this piece was never in the Collection, stockists did sell them on to collectors, hence their secondary market value.
MARKINGS: None.

ISSUE PRICE:	NIL	$ NIL
CURRENT VALUE:	150 – 200	$300 – 500
UPDATE:	_____	

Stratford House in terracotta. This is Faith Winter's copy, marked on the base as Number One

The signed base of a Stratford House in terracotta. (Photograph courtesy of Patty and Bill Sauers)

Village Scene, the point-of-sale from which the 1987 free Guild piece derived. (Courtesy of Sue Jelfs)

The Coaching Inn on its candleholder base

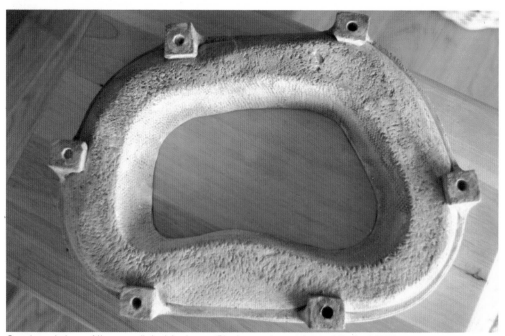

Overhead view of the candleholder base (Photograph courtesy of Patty & Bill Sauers)

The card dispenser sculpted by David Winter as a Point of Sale in 1984. Very few are known to exist.
(Photograph courtesy of John Hine Studios – dispenser courtesy of Denise Hutchings)

The Forge with the name plaque - a very rare piece. (Courtesy of Chris Billins)

The first David Winter Cottages Point of Sale. (Courtesy of Bob Lambrecht)

Market Street in its restyled (left) and original versions. (Original courtesy of Denise Hutchings)

The Winemerchant in its original (left) and restyled versions. (Original courtesy of Denise Hutchings)

Tudor Manor House – original (left) and restyled versions. (Original courtesy of Denise Hutchings)

Tudor Manor House – Rear view

Single Oast in its original (left) and restyled versions. (Original courtesy of Chris Billins)

Early back stamps

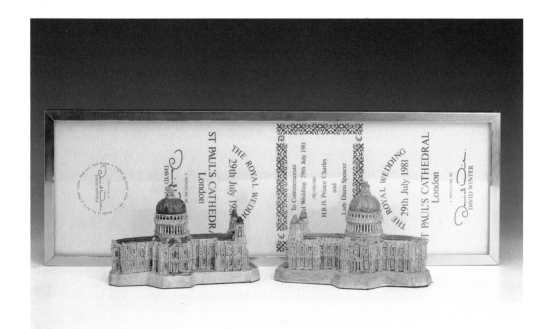

St Paul's Cathedral in two colour variations. Behind them is the wrap-around for the box. (St Paul's Cathedral courtesy of Denise Hutchings and Chris Billins. Wrap-around courtesy of David Winter)

William Shakespeare's Birthplace in tiny, medium and large sizes. The medium was sculpted by Malcolm Cooper. (Medium courtesy of Denise Hutchings)

The original (left) and restyled versions of The Village as seen from above. The differences – the lost buttress, the shortened cottage at the front and the ivy arches – can be clearly seen by comparing the two. (Original courtesy of Chris Billins)

14 - JOHN HINE STUDIOS

Early in 1986 work began on converting a set of dilapidated farm buildings in Aldershot into a permanent site for the 'Studio' (i.e. creative) side of John Hine Limited, as opposed to the 'Workshop' (production) concern, which was then firmly rooted at Woolmer Way, Bordon. The location was on the corner of two roads – Hillside Road and Eggars Hill – and although the postal address was (and still is) Hillside Road, it has always been known as Eggars Hill.

In the ensuing six years Eggars Hill has had many and various functions – but throughout its ever-developing role it has essentially been John Hine's workplace. Since the mid-80s, David Winter has preferred to work in his Home Studio and has sculpted very little at Eggars Hill. In contrast the beautiful seventeenth century barn has housed most of John Hine Studios' other artists at one stage or another, including Moe Wideman during a year long stay.

Today Eggars Hill has become primarily a visitors centre, and for 'David Winter' collectors the only place they will ever see a complete (well almost!) display of all David's released work. Even John Hine Studios don't own a Provencal Two!

As well as the opportunity to inspect the Retired Collection, organised tours of Eggars Hill include a demonstration of how David Winter Cottages are made, plus displays of other John Hine Studios artists – Malcolm Cooper, Christopher Lawrence, Moe Wideman, Sandra Kuck, Steve Kenyon and others.

Tours of Eggars Hill are completely free of charge and include morning coffee or afternoon tea. They commence at 10am and 2pm seven days a week, and if you are planning a visit it is advisable to book a place in advance – especially during the summer months.

A recent venture is an in-house shop which sells memorabilia not only of Eggars Hill itself but also of David Winter Cottages, most of which are unobtainable elsewhere (postcards, prints etc.). Cottages are also available for purchase, but on a restricted basis and mainly to first-time buyers; customers are then given details of stockists in their area. The idea is to give visitors who are not collectors the chance to begin a collection at Eggars Hill and then continue in their home area.

You are welcome to visit:
JOHN HINE STUDIOS
EGGARS HILL
2 HILLSIDE ROAD
ALDERSHOT
HAMPSHIRE GU11 3NB
TEL. (0252) 334672

Eggars Hill

Part of the display inside the seventeenth century barn

Grange Smashing

John Hine attacks a Grange, watched by Harry Hine

A sight to bring tears to the eyes of any David Winter collector – hundreds of previously perfect Granges lying smashed in a skip

When the decision to make a 'sudden death' retirement of The Grange was made on 20th June 1989, John Hine was in America. He phoned David Gravelle and asked for all models still in production to be delivered to his house; it took one and a half van loads. (John returned home some days later to find he couldn't open his front door for Granges.) That weekend, Harry Hine rented a skip, three pairs of goggles and three club hammers, and the best part of three days was spent smashing the pieces, with David Gravelle giving an impromptu running total of how much money they were saying good bye to. John's wife Rosie brought out a cup of tea for them and received a Grange for her trouble, the only piece to escape the cull. At least a thousand perfect pieces were destroyed and even more unpainted white stock.

The Collectors Book, in its two versions

The Placemats and Coasters. Illustrations by Michael Fisher

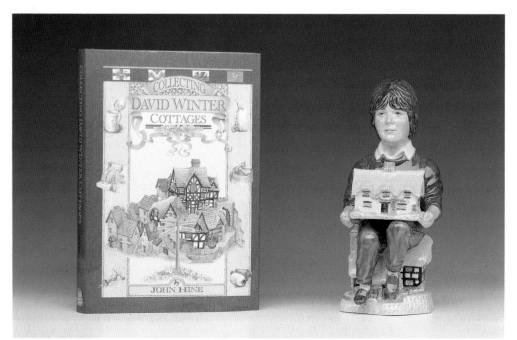

John Hine's Book Collecting David Winter Cottages with Toby Jug of David Winter by Kevin Francis Ceramics

The pack of David Winter cards produced in 1984

CASTLE IN THE AIR, David Winter's 1991 tour-de-force

AWARDS
RECEIVED BY DAVID WINTER COTTAGES
AND JOHN HINE STUDIOS

SMUGGLERS CREEK
Best Collectible of the Show 1987
The California Plate and Collectible Show,
Pasadena, California

DAVID WINTER COTTAGES
Collectible of the Year 1987 NALED
(National Association of Limited Edition Dealers)
International Plate and Collectible Exposition,
South Bend, Indiana

JOHN HINE LIMITED
Manufacturer of the Year 1987
NALED - South Bend, Indiana

JOHN HINE LIMITED
1988 Queen's Award for Export Achievement

David Winter Cottages
Collectible of the Show 1988
The California Plate and Collectible Show,
Pasadena, California

JOHN HINE LIMITED
Manufacturer of the Show 1988
The California Plate and Collectible Show,
Pasadena, California

HOGMANAY
Best Figurine 1988
The California Plate and Collectible Show,
Pasadena, California

DAVID WINTER COTTAGES
Collectible of the Year 1988
NALED - South Bend, Indiana

DAVID WINTER
Artist of the Year (1st Runner Up) 1988
NALED - South Bend, Indiana

DAVID WINTER COTTAGES
Collectible of the Show 1988
NALED - South Bend, Indiana

JOHN HINE LIMITED
Manufacturer of the Year 1988
NALED - South Bend, Indiana

HOGMANAY
Figurine of the Year 1989
NALED - South Bend, Indiana

DAVID WINTER
Artist of the Year (1st Runner Up) 1989
NALED - South Bend, Indiana

DAVID WINTER COTTAGES
Collectible of the Year (1st Runner Up) 1989
NALED - South Bend, Indiana

JOHN HINE LIMITED
Manufacturer of the Year (2nd Runner Up) 1989
NALED - South Bend, Indiana

A CHRISTMAS CAROL
Figurine of the Year 1990
NALED - South Bend, Indiana

DAVID WINTER COTTAGES
Collectible of the Year (1st Runner Up)
NALED - South Bend, Indiana 1990

DAVID WINTER
Artist of the Year (2nd Runner Up) 1990
NALED - South Bend, Indiana

DAVID WINTER COTTAGES
Collectible of the Show 1990
International Plate and Collectible Exposition,
Westchester, New York

FRED'S HOME
Cottage of the Show 1991
International Collectible Exposition,
Long Beach, California

DAVID WINTER
Artist of the Year 1991
NALED - South Bend, Indiana

DAVID WINTER COTTAGES
Collectable of the Show 1991
London Collectors Showcase, London

NOTES

NOTES

 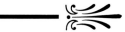

NOTES

NOTES

NOTES

NOTES

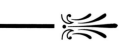

NOTES